W9-CEE-381

ADVANTAGE Math

Grade **5**

Table of Contents

Table of Contents

CREDITS

Concept Development: Kent Publishing Services, Inc.
Written by: Barbara Irvin, Ph.D.
Editor: Carla Hamaguchi
Designer/Production: Moonhee Pak/Carrie Carter
Illustrator: Corbin Hillam
Art Director: Tom Cochrane
Project Director: Carolea Williams

Introduction

The Advantage Math Series for grades 3–6 offers instruction and practice for key skills in each math strand recommended by the National Council for Teachers of Mathematics (NCTM), including

- numeration and number theory
- operations
- geometry
- measurement
- patterns, functions, and algebra
- data analysis and probability
- problem solving

Take a look at all the advantages this math series offers . . .

Strong Skill Instruction

- The **teaching component** at the top of the activity pages provides the support students need to work through the book independently.

- Plenty of **skill practice** pages will ensure students master essential math computation skills they need to increase their math fluency.

- A **problem-solving strand** is woven within skill practice pages to offer students an opportunity to practice critical thinking skills.

teaching
component

skill
practice

problem
solving

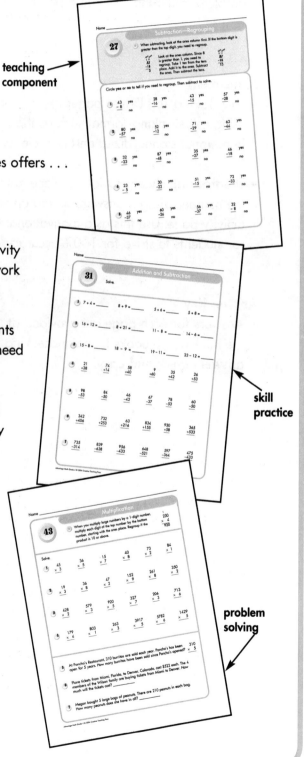

Introduction

- **Mixed-practice pages** include a variety of math concepts on one workbook page. This challenges students to think through each problem rather than rely on a predictable format.

Assessment

- The "Take a Test Drive" pages provide practice using a **test-taking** format such as those included in national standardized and proficiency tests.

- The **tracking sheet** provides a place to record the number of right answers scored on each activity page. Use this as a motivational tool for students to strive for 100% accuracy.

Answer Key

- Answers for each page are provided at the back of the books to make **checking answers quick and easy.**

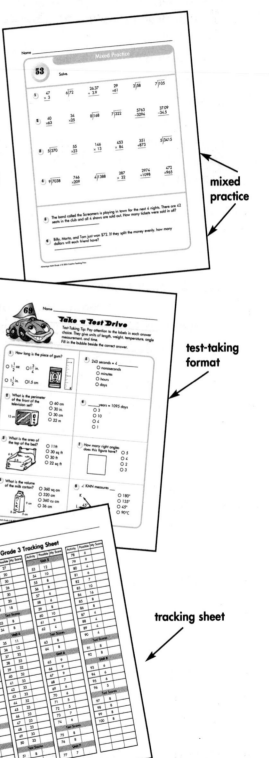

mixed practice

test-taking format

tracking sheet

Place Value

1

	Millions			Thousands			Ones	
Hundreds	Tens	Ones	Hundreds	Tens	Ones	Hundreds	Tens	Ones
7	0	3	6	5	1	8	9	6

Standard form: 703,651,896

Short word form: 703 million, 651 thousand, 896

Expanded form: 700,000,000 + 3,000,000 + 600,000 + 50,000 + 1,000 + 800 + 90 + 6

Write each number in standard form.

1 65 thousand, 4 hundred, 9 _____

2 20,000,000 + 6,000,000 + 500,000 + 3,000 + 70 _____

3 three hundred eighty million, forty-five _____

4 70,000,000 + 70,000 + 70 _____

5 932 million, 408 thousand _____

6 400,000,000 + 300,000 + 700 _____

Write the value of the 3 in each number.

7 4,386 _____   43,086 _____

8 403,806 _____   37,402,088 _____

9 837,604 _____   6,478,531 _____

10 Earth is about ninety-three million miles from the sun. Write the number in standard form. _____

11 Mars is 141,710,000 miles from the sun. Write the number in short word form.

_____

Compare and Order Numbers

2

⭐ Compare 3,748 and 3,487. Which number is greater?

3,748	**7** hundreds > **4** hundreds	> greater than
3,487	3,748 > 3,487	< less than
	3,748 is greater than 3,487	= equals

Complete the number sentence.

1 842 ◯ 598   423 ◯ 424

2 736 ◯ 763   1,234 ◯ 2,143

3 6,408 ◯ 6,840   83,303 ◯ 83,033

4 137,627 ◯ 141,672   573,240 ◯ 572,304

5 9,612,924 ◯ 9,596,999   45,866,854 ◯ 45,686,854

Order the numbers from least to greatest.

6 834, 348, 843, 438 _____

7 45,672 46,762 45,692 _____

8 327,605 325,750 325,805 _____

9 1,375,671 1,373,917 1,375,617 _____

10 63,367 63,736 67,673 67,376 _____

11 Grant School has 1,248 students. Lincoln School has 2,104 students. Franklin School has 1,099 students. Which school has the greatest number of students? _____

12 Which school has the least number of students? _____

Name _____

Estimate Sums and Differences

3 To estimate, round numbers, then add or subtract.

Estimate: 729 + 1,853
  700 + 2,000 = 2,700
  729 + 1,853 is *about* 2,700.

Estimate. Write the rounded numbers and the sum or difference.

1 5,095 + 836   _____ + _____ = _____

2 4,365 – 1,706   _____ – _____ = _____

3 1,143 – 683   _____ – _____ = _____

4 23,087 + 6,999   _____ + _____ = _____

5 372,000 – 99,995   _____ – _____ = _____

6 408,973 + 48,073   _____ + _____ = _____

Estimate the sum or difference.

7 586 + 3,205 _____   7,386 – 971 _____

8 17,400 – 6,035 _____   34,605 + 19,543 _____

9 36,087 – 8,034 _____   3,572 + 8,124 _____

10 326,799 – 188,000 _____   492,765 + 603,091 _____

11 The cafeteria served 894 bananas and 1,237 apples during lunch. About how much fruit was served? _____

12 One day, 4,326 people ate at the cafeteria. The next day, 3,784 people ate there. About how many people ate at the cafeteria during those two days?

_____

Add and Subtract Numbers

4

⭐ Find the difference of 26,053 and 12,786.

Subtract ones. Regroup if needed.	Subtract tens. Regroup if needed.	Subtract hundreds. Regroup if needed.	Subtract thousands.	Subtract ten thousands.
4 13	9 14 13	5 9 14 13	5 9 14 13	5 9 14 13
26,05̶3̶	26,0̶5̶3̶	2̶6̶,0̶5̶3̶	2̶6̶,0̶5̶3̶	2̶6̶,0̶5̶3̶ minuend
−12,786	−12,786	−12,786	−12,786	−12,786 minuend
7	67	267	3,267	13,267 difference

Find the sums and differences.

1

97	56	386	716	684	278
+45	−29	+636	−649	−294	+103

2

326	3,645	73,864	60,216	4,827	7,821
+845	− 1,248	+16,136	−39,583	+1,608	−2,039

3

2,284	9,352	6,833	48,956	43,276	630,017
−2,159	−3,673	+2,960	−27,680	+592,037	− 54,260

4

40,352	57,293	938,774	629,274	268,934	865,733
−36,064	+65,296	−625,803	+ 13,492	−145,089	−453,924

5 Bigg City has a population of 349,673. When Bigg College is in session, the population jumps to 398,412. How many people go to Bigg College?

_____

6 During summer school at Bigg College, 2,948 students stay to take classes. 835 students stay to work. How many students stay during the summer?

_____

Estimate Products

5

 To estimate products, round factors to their greatest place and use the correct number of zeros.

Estimate: 6,249 x 3
$$6,000 \times 3 = 18,000$$
6,249 x 3 is *about* 18,000.

Estimate. Write the rounded factors and the products.

1 6 x 838   _____ x _____ = _____

2 4,832 x 9   _____ x _____ = _____

3 430 x 50   _____ x _____ = _____

4 578 x 96   _____ x _____ = _____

5 704 x 36   _____ x _____ = _____

6 583 x 65   _____ x _____ = _____

Estimate the product.

7 2 x 492 = _____   567 x 36 = _____

8 67 x 298 = _____   5,723 x 51 = _____

9 2,631 x 72 = _____   4,057 x 3,112 = _____

10 7,280 x 3,788 = _____   82 x 2,900 = _____

11 Each worker at the widget factory makes about 3,945 widgets every day. If there are about 53 workers at the factory, about how many widgets are made each day? _____

12 About 15 workers work overtime at the factory. If these workers can make 4,321 widgets every day, about how many widgets do these workers make each day?

_____

Name _____

6

⭐ Find the **product** of 628 and 79.

Multiply by the ones. Regroup if needed.	Multiply by the tens. Regroup if needed.	Add the products. Regroup if needed.
2 7	1 5	
628	**628**	628 factor
× **79**	× **79**	× 79 factor
5,652	5,652	5,652 product
	+**43,960**	+43,960
		49,612

Multiply. Regroup when needed.

1
71	64	346	509	7,243	5,403
×36	×15	× 57	× 46	× 81	× 21

2
92	809	315	652	287	721
×34	× 31	× 76	× 49	× 35	× 15

3
692	490	267	519	673	311
×418	×426	×339	×437	×638	×704

4 3,492 workers eat in the factory cafeteria each day. On chili day, each person gets 8 crackers. How many crackers are served on chili day? _____

5 Some factory workers wear gloves. If these 240 workers work 293 days each year, how many pairs of gloves are needed altogether every year? _____

Estimate Quotients

7 ⭐ To estimate quotients, round the dividend and the divisor to compatible numbers.

Round one or both of the numbers, so that one number is divisible by the other.
Estimate: 1,776 ÷ 28

Think of the basic fact 18 ÷ 3. **1,800 ÷ 30**

Think of basic division facts and use the correct number of zeros.
1,800 ÷ **3**0 = **6**0

1,776 ÷ 28 is *about* 60.

Estimate. Write the rounded numbers and quotients.

1   391 ÷ 82
_____ ÷ _____ = _____

391 ÷ 48
_____ ÷ _____ = _____

2   5,360 ÷ 39
_____ ÷ _____ = _____

784 ÷ 83
_____ ÷ _____ = _____

3   2,239 ÷ 77
_____ ÷ _____ = _____

8,042 ÷ 17
_____ ÷ _____ = _____

Estimate the quotient.

4   285 ÷ 29 = _____

1,395 ÷ 47 = _____

5   52)5,325 = _____

48)2,501 = _____

6   3,570 ÷ 47= _____

935 ÷ 89 = _____

---

7   Julia has 158 baseball cards. If a collector's book holds about 51 cards, about how many books does she need to hold all her cards? _____

8   The baseball card collecting club has 3,120 cards to trade. If each person has about 30 cards to trade, about how many people are in the club? _____

Divide Numbers

8

⭐ Find the quotient for 2,585 ÷ 27.

Divide.
Multiply. Subtract.
Bring down.

$$\begin{array}{r} 9 \\ 27\overline{)2,585} \\ -243 \\ \hline 155 \end{array}$$

Repeat the steps
until finished.

$$\begin{array}{r} 95\,R\,20 \\ 27\overline{)2,585} \\ -243 \\ \hline 155 \\ -135 \\ \hline 20 \end{array}$$

Check by multiplying.

$$\begin{array}{r} 95 \\ \times 27 \\ \hline 665 \\ +1,900 \\ \hline 2,565 \\ +\;\;\;20 \\ \hline 2,585 \end{array}$$

Find the quotient.

1 $3\overline{)72}$ $5\overline{)95}$ $8\overline{)272}$ $60\overline{)240}$

2 $22\overline{)154}$ $17\overline{)136}$ $25\overline{)750}$ $42\overline{)1,260}$

3 $79\overline{)4,424}$ $32\overline{)2,516}$ $86\overline{)5,762}$ $92\overline{)4,144}$

4 $28\overline{)10,625}$ $86\overline{)9,050}$ $29\overline{)3,019}$ $36\overline{)25,850}$

5 There are 450 students at Fair Park School. If there are 25 students in each class, how many classes are there? _____

6 The school system has 1,470 students. If each school bus holds 35 students, how many buses do they need? _____

Variables and Expressions

A **variable** is a letter or symbol used to represent a number. An **algebraic expression** contains variables and numbers. It has no equal sign. You can solve, or **evaluate, an expression** when the variable represents a certain number.

word phrase
"three plus a number"

algebraic expression
$3 + n$
variable

evaluate an expression
What is $3 + n$ when $n = 5$?
$3 + n$
$3 + 5 = 8$

Write an algebraic expression for each word phrase.

1 nine less than a number _____

2 a number divided by three _____

3 six more than a number _____

4 six times a number _____

5 a number minus four _____

6 twice a number _____

Evaluate each expression when $n = 12$.

7 $n + 8$ _____ $n \div 4$ _____ $3n$ _____

8 $20 - n$ _____ $\frac{1}{3} n$ _____ $n + 0$ _____

Evaluate.

9 What is $6w$ when $w = 8$? _____   What is $k - 9$ when $k = 15$? _____

10 What is $n \div 3$ when $n = 24$? _____   What is $6 + g$ when $g = 14$? _____

Solve Equations

10

⭐ An **equation** is a number sentence with an equal sign. To solve an equation, use **inverse operations**.

To solve an addition equation, subtract the same number from each side. Solve: $n + 5 = 8$	$$\begin{array}{r} n + 5 = 8 \\ -5 \quad -5 \\ \hline n = 3 \end{array}$$	To solve a multiplication equation, divide each side by the same number. Solve: $5t = 20$	$$\frac{5t}{5} = \frac{20}{5}$$ $$t = 4$$
To solve a subtraction equation, add the same number to each side. Solve: $h - 4 = 6$	$$\begin{array}{r} h - 4 = 6 \\ +4 \quad +4 \\ \hline h = 10 \end{array}$$	To solve a division equation, multiply each side by the same number. Solve: $\frac{m}{3} = 5$	$$\frac{m}{3} \times 3 = 5 \times 3$$ $$m = 15$$

Solve the equations.

1 $a + 5 = 17$ $6t = 72$ $83 - d = 22$
   $a = $ _____ $t = $ _____ $d = $ _____

2 $c + 30 = 76$ $5w = 0$ $n \div 3 = 8$
   $c = $ _____ $w = $ _____ $n = $ _____

3 $7h = 7$ $^m/_4 = 20$ $3p = 66$
   $h = $ _____ $m = $ _____ $p = $ _____

4 $m - 43 = 17$ $20n = 600$ $\frac{1}{2}k = 40$
   $m = $ _____ $n = $ _____ $k = $ _____

5 $17 + c = 35$ $\frac{1}{3}k = 18$ $4w = 12$
   $c = $ _____ $k = $ _____ $w = $ _____

6 $100 - d = 46$ $\frac{1}{5}r = 1$ $^x/_2 = 45$
   $d = $ _____ $r = $ _____ $x = $ _____

Mixed Practice

11

Solve.

1

5,346
−1,409

413
× 69

4,539
+4,761

$82\overline{)2,640}$

2

6,543
×   9

75,814
+15,556

$36\overline{)5,112}$

25,000
− 7,567

3

60,537
−29,395

609
× 83

37,567
490
+ 5,065

$31\overline{)25,080}$

4

47,070
−29,980

703
× 46

$48\overline{)25,000}$

849
27,075
+ 6,503

5 $a + 30 = 76$ $8t = 40$ $d − 14 = 52$ $n \div 6 = 6$

6 The cooks only have 23,572 blueberries for the pancake breakfast. If they plan on having about 837 people, **about** how many blueberries will each person get?

_____

7 The cooks only have 23,572 blueberries for the pancake breakfast. If they plan on having 837 people, **exactly** how many blueberries will each person get?

_____

Story Problems

12 ⭐ On Arbor Day, Jason and Ramon planted 155 small trees. If Ramon planted 78 trees, how many trees did Jason plant?

Let j = trees Jason planted

$$78 + j = 155$$
$$-78 \qquad -78$$
$$j = 77$$

Jason planted 77 trees.

Understand: Read the problem. What do you have to find?

Plan: Choose the operation. Write an equation.

Solve: Find and label the answer.

Check: Is the answer reasonable? Does the solution answer the question?

Solve.

1 A media store sells about 45 CDs per hour. About how many CDs will it sell in 8 hours? _____

2 Jenny and Megan played a computer game. Jenny scored 356 points and Megan scored 508 points. How many more points did Megan score? _____

3 Three buses took students to the museum. Bus 1 had 43 students and Buses 2 and 3 had 42 students each. How many students went to the museum? _____

4 The Ojeda family traveled 364 miles on 14 gallons of gas. How many miles per gallon was that? _____

5 Tyler and his friends played laser tag all day. Tyler scored 1,254 points; Lucas scored 1,305 points; Brandon scored 987 points; and Garrett scored 1,095 points. Write their scores in order from greatest to least. _____

6 What was Tyler's team score? (Hint: A team score is the sum of the scores for all players on the team.) _____

Take a Test Drive

Test-Taking Tip: Fill in only one bubble and fill it in completely.

Fill in the bubble beside the correct answer.

---

1 Which is 2,000,000 + 60,000 + 5,000 + 90 in standard form?

- ○ 265,090
- ○ 2,060,590
- ○ 2,065,090
- ○ 2,605,090

2 What is the value of the 3 in 673,401?

- ○ 300
- ○ 3,000
- ○ 30,000
- ○ 300,000

3 Which number is greater than 46,762?

- ○ 46,749
- ○ 46,753
- ○ 46,762
- ○ 46,770

4 Which set of numbers is in order from least to greatest?

- ○ 83,303 83,033 83,330
- ○ 83,033 83,303 83,330
- ○ 83,033 83,330 83,303
- ○ 83,033 83,333 83,330

5 Which number is a good estimate for 1,893 + 513?

- ○ 1,500
- ○ 1,600
- ○ 2,500
- ○ 2,600

6 Which number is a good estimate for 712 x 47?

- ○ 24,000
- ○ 28,000
- ○ 35,000
- ○ 40,000

7 Which is a good way to estimate 6,336 – 2,973?

- ○ 6,000 – 2,000
- ○ 6,000 – 3,000
- ○ 7,000 – 2,000
- ○ 7,000 – 3,000

8 Which basic division fact can you use to estimate 2,405 ÷ 370?

- ○ 24 ÷ 4
- ○ 28 ÷ 4
- ○ 25 ÷ 5
- ○ 30 ÷ 5

Name _____

Take a Test Drive

Fill in the bubble beside the correct answer.

1 5,073 – 2,546 =
- ○ 2,427
- ○ 2,527
- ○ 3,533
- ○ 7,619

2 473 × 69 =
- ○ 4,257
- ○ 7,095
- ○ 32,507
- ○ 32,637

3 73,206 + 591 + 9,003 =
- ○ 73,797
- ○ 82,209
- ○ 82,800
- ○ 83,700

4 4,350 ÷ 58 =
- ○ 63
- ○ 75
- ○ 74
- ○ 76

5 Which operation would you use to check the answer to 1,817 ÷ 23?
- ○ addition
- ○ subtraction
- ○ multiplication
- ○ division

6 What is 2n when n = 12?
- ○ 6
- ○ 10
- ○ 14
- ○ 24

7 If n ÷ 4 = 8, then n = _____.
- ○ 2
- ○ 4
- ○ 12
- ○ 32

8 There were 456 fans at a swim meet on Tuesday and 374 fans on Friday. How many more fans were at the swim meet on Tuesday?
- ○ 830
- ○ 111
- ○ 82
- ○ 24

Place Value

15

hundreds 100	tens 10	ones 1		tenths 1/10	hundredths 1/100	thousandths 1/1,000
	3	7	.	0	6	
4	1	6	.	7		
		0	.	2	3	5

The 3 in 0.235 is in the hundredths place.
The value of 3 in 0.235 is 0.03 or 3/100.

Write each number in standard form.

1 42 hundredths _____   4 and 8 thousandths _____

2 567 thousandths _____   ten and one tenth _____

3 7 hundred _____   7 hundredths _____

Name the place of the 5 in each number.

4 3.52 _____   0.352 _____

5 65.09 _____   7.005 _____

6 753.4 _____   0.051 _____

Write the value of the 7 in each number as a decimal and a fraction.

7 0.37 _____ , _____   1.735 _____ , _____

8 6.075 _____ , _____   27.05 _____ , _____

9 0.127 _____ , _____   3.007 _____ , _____

Compare and Order Decimals

16

⭐ Compare 3.5 and 3.15.
3.5 = 3.50

3.50   **5** tenths > **1** tenth
3.15   3.5 > 3.15
        3.5 is greater than 3.15.

Complete the number sentence with <, =, or >.

1 3.65 ◯ 36.5   8.03 ◯ 8.3

2 0.438 ◯ 0.43   0.005 ◯ 0.500

3 4.73 ◯ 4.073   0.300 ◯ 0.030

4 6.2 ◯ 6.162   23.05 ◯ 2.305

Order the decimals from least to greatest.

5 4.007 4.7 4.07 _____

6 6.4 0.64 6.04 _____

7 0.09 0.90 0.009 _____

8 7.503 7.053 75.03 _____

9 2.016 2.6 2.36 _____

10 Maddy only needed the smallest amount of medicine for her gerbil. The medicine comes in bottles with 1.5 ounces, 2.0 ounces, and 0.75 ounce. Which amount should Maddy get? _____

11 Maddy kept track of how much water her gerbil drank. Between noon and 1:00, Trog drank 0.04 ounce of water. By 2:00, Trog drank 0.02 ounce. By 3:00, Trog drank 0.1 ounce. When did Trog drink the most water? _____

Estimate Decimal Sums and Differences

17

⭐ Estimate: $7.87 – $0.69

$$\begin{array}{cc} \$7.87 & \$8 \\ -\ 0.69 & -1 \\ \hline & \$7 \end{array}$$

$7.87 – $0.69 is about $7.

Estimate. Write the rounded decimals and the sum or difference.

1

$$\begin{array}{l} 6.8 \rightarrow \\ +3.05 \rightarrow \underline{\hspace{1cm}} \end{array} \qquad \begin{array}{l} 8.097 \rightarrow \\ -1.83 \ \rightarrow \underline{\hspace{1cm}} \end{array} \qquad \begin{array}{l} 2.5 \ \rightarrow \\ -0.73 \rightarrow \underline{\hspace{1cm}} \end{array}$$

2

$$\begin{array}{l} \$6.25 \rightarrow \\ +1.75 \rightarrow \underline{\hspace{1cm}} \end{array} \qquad \begin{array}{l} \$9.63 \rightarrow \\ -8.04 \rightarrow \underline{\hspace{1cm}} \end{array} \qquad \begin{array}{l} 3.075 \rightarrow \\ -0.18 \ \rightarrow \underline{\hspace{1cm}} \end{array}$$

Estimate the sums and differences.

3   5.03 + 0.7 _____ $4.79 – $1.83 _____

4   6.056 – 1.9 _____   3.089 + 3.9 _____

5 $1.37 + $0.55 _____   8.3 – 0.73 _____

---

6   Joey made $8.50 mowing the lawn. He made $5.25 for doing other chores. About how much did he make? _____

7   Joey bought a mystery book for $1.85 and a CD for $11.60. About how much did Joey spend? _____

Name _____

18

Line up the decimal points.	Subtract. Regroup if needed.	Write the decimal point in the answer.
Subtract: 0.8 – 0.53 0.80 $\underline{-0.53}$	$\overset{7\ 10}{0.8\cancel{0}}$ $\underline{-0.53}$ 27	$\overset{7\ 10}{0.8\cancel{0}}$ $\underline{-0.53}$ 0.27

Find the sums and differences.

1

3.8	7.53	5.26	6.821	$7.25	$4.35
+4.16	–2.49	+0.9	–0.39	–$1.49	+$7.22

2

0.73	5.7	5.07	6	1.35	2.1
+0.006	–0.06	+4	–1.37	0.7	0.728
				+0.069	+0.7

3

7.65	5.03	0.743	1.569	6	9.23
–4.069	+0.76	–0.36	4.17	+0.378	–1.2
			+3.2		

4

6	$3.25	0.42	0.5	6.7	$8.46
–0.378	–2	+0.09	–0.18	+7.06	–$6.96

5 Ben bought juice for $1.35. He gave the cashier $5. How much change should he receive? _____

6 Grace's rain gauge collected 1.3 inches of rain. Later, it rained another 0.5 inch. How much rain would be in the rain gauge now? _____

Multiply Decimals by 10, 100, and 1,000

19

⭐ Here are some shortcuts to help you multiply by powers of 10.

Multiply by	Move decimal point to the **right**	
10	1 place	10 x 3.86 = 38.6 10 x 0.006 = 0.06
100	2 places	100 x 3.86 = 386 100 x 0.006 = 0.6
1,000	3 places	1,000 x 3.860 = 3,860 1,000 x 0.006 = 6

Write the products.

1. 3.26 x 10 = _____   0.46 x 10 = _____

   3.26 x 100 = _____   0.46 x 100 = _____

   3.26 x 1,000 = _____   0.46 x 1,000 = _____

Write the products.

2.

Multiply by 10		Multiply by 100		Multiply by 1,000	
Input	Output	Input	Output	Input	Output
3.8	_____	4.2	_____	1.5	_____
0.62	_____	0.76	_____	0.032	_____
0.14	_____	0.035	_____	0.75	_____

Write the products.

3. 2.5 x 10 = _____   0.47 x 10 = _____   1.7 x 1,000 = _____

4. 0.7 x 100 = _____   8.06 x 10 = _____   0.083 x 100 = _____

5. 1.59 x 1,000 = _____   3.83 x 100 = _____   6.008 x 10 = _____

6. 100 x 8.32 = _____   4.16 x 1,000 = _____   1,000 x 0.05 = _____

Divide Decimals by 10, 100, and 1,000

20

⭐ Here are some shortcuts to help you divide by powers of 10.

Divide by	Move decimal point to the **left**	
10	1 place	$83.45 \div 10 = 8.345$
100	2 places	$83.45 \div 100 = 0.8345$
1,000	3 places	$083.45 \div 1,000 = 0.08345$

Solve.

1. $2,705 \div 10 =$ _____ $35.17 \div 10 =$ _____ $2,705 \div 100 =$ _____

2. $35.17 \div 100 =$ _____ $2,705 \div 1,000 =$ _____ $35.17 \div 1,000 =$ _____

3. $2.37 \div 10 =$ _____ $758 \div 100 =$ _____ $43 \div 10 =$ _____

4. $4,256 \div 1,000 =$ _____ $38.6 \div 10 =$ _____ $745.1 \div 100 =$ _____

5. $63.2 \div 100 =$ _____ $5.8 \div 1,000 =$ _____ $30.8 \div 1,000 =$ _____

6. $8.6 \div 100 =$ _____ $326.2 \div 100 =$ _____ $0.75 \div 10 =$ _____

7. $37 \div 10 =$ _____ $75.8 \div 10 =$ _____ $0.46 \div 1,000 =$ _____

8. $835.1 \div 100 =$ _____ $3.8 \div 100 =$ _____ $4,305 \div 1,000 =$ _____

9. $0.009 \div 100 =$ _____ $75.06 \div 10 =$ _____ $0.105 \div 100 =$ _____

10. $3.056 \div 10 =$ _____ $3.62 \div 100 =$ _____ $1,002 \div 1,000 =$ _____

11. Bagels are $0.45 each. How much do 10 cost? _____

12. Bagels cost $0.45 each. The bakery sold 100 bagels this morning. How much money did the bakery make? _____

Name _____

Estimate Decimal Products

21

⭐ To estimate decimals, round the factors to whole numbers.
Estimate: 3.7 x 9.083
↓　↓
4 x 9 = 36
3.7 x 9.083 is about 36.

Estimate. Write the rounded factors and the products.

1. 4.2 x 8.03
_____ x _____ = _____

   $8.79 x 3.5
_____ x _____ = _____

2. 5.006 x 5.6
_____ x _____ = _____

   8.4 x $5.67
_____ x _____ = _____

3. 1.4 x 3.45
_____ x _____ = _____

   6.701 x 2.8
_____ x _____ = _____

Estimate the products.

4. 7.26 x 4.3 _____

   $1.29 x 7.05 _____

5. 3.21 x 6.5 _____

   2.803 x $4.83 _____

6. 0.75 x 29 _____

   4.6 x 9.9 _____

7. Chloe is making some curtains. She needs 18 yards of fabric that costs $5.95 a yard. She has $100. Can she buy all the fabric? Explain. _____
_____

8. Abdul is making a bookcase. He needs 26 feet of boards that cost $2.75 a foot. He has $75. Can Abdul buy all the boards? Explain._____
_____

Name _____

22

★ Find the product of 2.61 and 3.2.

$$\begin{array}{r} 2.61 \leftarrow 2 \text{ places} \\ \times\ 3.2 \leftarrow 1 \text{ place} \\ \hline 522 \\ +7830 \\ \hline 8.352 \leftarrow 3 \text{ places} \end{array}$$

Find the products.

1

2.9	3.14	0.8	0.73	4.7	2.1
×3.7	×6.2	×0.7	×3.2	×0.5	×0.3

2

$6.29	4.03	$0.37	26.7	0.04	78.31
× 8.3	×0.6	× 52	× 4.3	× 1.2	× 22

3

1.85	$23.95	0.17	$0.80	0.06	5.05
× 9.2	× 6	× 0.5	× 35	×0.04	×0.27

4

57	1.3	0.6	$1.50	4.5	$9.97
×0.5	×3.3	×12	× 10	×20	× 3

5 Lunch costs $3.50 in the cafeteria. How much do 5 lunches cost? _____

6 An extra apple costs $0.25. How much do 7 apples cost? _____

Divide Decimals

23

⭐ Find the quotient for 57.6 ÷ 45.

Place decimal point in the quotient.	Divide.	Check by multiplying.
45)57.6	1.28 45)57.60 −45 126 −90 360 −360 0	1.28 × 45 640 +5120 57.60

Find the quotients.

1 5)6.85   6)$8.52   5)3.155   6)12.48   12)$5.04   23)3.45

2 8)0.12   71)1.136   5)48.3   9)$30.78   51)207.06   11)30.69

3 The Buntz family paid $26.25 for movie tickets. If there are 5 people in the family, how much did each ticket cost? _____

4 Logan, Aaron, and Sophie shared a bucket of popcorn. If the popcorn cost $4.50 and the children each paid the same amount, how much did each share of popcorn cost? _____

Name _____

24

Solve.

1
| 7.5 | 6.35 | 6.8 | 3.026 |
| +2.89 | −1.83 | −3.05 | +1.98 |

2
| $15.25 | 7.26 | 8)41.92 | 1.3 |
| − 8.79 | × 4.3 | | ×0.05 |

3
| 32)68.8 | 7 | $6.39 | 18)37.62 |
| | −5.87 | × 15 | |

4   2.69 x 1,000 = _____   483.6 ÷ 100 = _____

Order the numbers from least to greatest.

5   5.07   7.05   7.5   0.57 _____

6   395   3.95   0.395   39.5 _____

7   0.17   0.017   1.70   170 _____

8   0.45   0.532   0.451   0.4 _____

25

Take a Test Drive

Test-Taking Tip: If you change an answer, be sure to completely erase the incorrect answer.

Fill in the bubble beside the correct answer.

1 What is "35 hundredths" in standard form?
- ○ 3,500
- ○ 35.00
- ○ 0.35
- ○ 0.035

2 What is the place of the 8 in 25.836?
- ○ tens
- ○ tenths
- ○ hundredths
- ○ thousandths

3 What is the value of the 6 in 8.367?
- ○ 6 tenths
- ○ 60 tenths
- ○ 6 hundredths
- ○ 60 hundredths

4 Which is the same as 2.6?
- ○ 2.006
- ○ 2.06
- ○ 2.60
- ○ 2.060

5 Which sign shows how the two decimals compare to each other?
8.063 ___ 8.63
- ○ <
- ○ >
- ○ =
- ○ +

6 Which set of decimals is in order from least to greatest?
- ○ 4.9 4.90 4.900
- ○ 4.9 4.09 4.009
- ○ 4.009 4.09 4.9
- ○ 4.900 4.090 4.009

7 To multiply a decimal by 100, move the decimal point _____.
- ○ 1 place to the right
- ○ 2 places to the right
- ○ 3 places to the right
- ○ 3 places to the left

8 358.2 ÷ 10 = _____
- ○ 3.5820
- ○ 3,520
- ○ 35.82
- ○ 3.582

Take a Test Drive

Fill in the bubble beside the correct answer.

1 Which is a good estimate for 8.037 + 0.05?
- ○ 0.08
- ○ 0.8
- ○ 8
- ○ 9

5 4.07 × 3.6
- ○ 4.43
- ○ 7.67
- ○ 14.652
- ○ 16.92

2 Which is a good estimate for 4.75 × 1.063?
- ○ 4
- ○ 5
- ○ 10
- ○ 5,000

6 0.09 × 0.8
- ○ 0.72
- ○ 0.89
- ○ 0.072
- ○ 0.089

3 6.3 +2.57
- ○ 3.20
- ○ 3.73
- ○ 8.87
- ○ 16.191

7 $4)\overline{10.96}$
- ○ 0.274
- ○ 2.74
- ○ 27.4
- ○ 274

4 4.5 −3.07
- ○ 0.43
- ○ 1.43
- ○ 2.62
- ○ 7.57

8 $71)\overline{22.72}$
- ○ 0.032
- ○ 0.32
- ○ 3.2
- ○ 32

Name _____

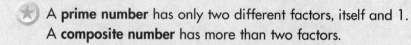

Find Prime Numbers

27

⭐ A **prime number** has only two different factors, itself and 1.
A **composite number** has more than two factors.

1	2	3	4	5	6	7	8	9	10
11	12	13	14	15	16	17	18	19	20
21	22	23	24	25	26	27	28	29	30
31	32	33	34	35	36	37	38	39	40
41	42	43	44	45	46	47	48	49	50
51	52	53	54	55	56	57	58	59	60
61	62	63	64	65	66	67	68	69	70
71	72	73	74	75	76	77	78	79	80
81	82	83	84	85	86	87	88	89	90
91	92	93	94	95	96	97	98	99	100

1 Cross out 1. It has only 1 factor. It is neither prime nor composite.

2 Circle 2. Then, cross out all the numbers divisible by 2.

3 Go to the next number that is not circled or crossed out and circle it. Then, cross out all the numbers divisible by that number.

4 Repeat step 3 until you find all the prime numbers less than 100.

5 How many prime numbers did you find? _____

6 What is the least prime number? _____ Greatest prime number? _____

7 List the prime numbers less than 30.

_____ _____ _____ _____ _____ _____ _____ _____ _____ _____

8 List the prime numbers between 30 and 100.

_____ _____ _____ _____ _____ _____ _____ _____ _____ _____

_____ _____ _____ _____ _____

Prime and Composite Numbers

28

⭐ A **prime number** has only two different factors, itself and 1.
$2 = 2 \times 1$ $13 = 13 \times 1$ $29 = 29 \times 1$

A **composite number** has more than two factors.
$12 = 12 \times 1$ and $12 = 6 \times 2$ and $12 = 4 \times 3$
1, 2, 3, 4, 6, and 12 are factors of 12.

Find all the factors. Then, write whether the number is prime or composite.

1 23 _____, _____

2 32 _____, _____

3 37 _____, _____

⭐ A **factor tree** can be used to find prime factors of a composite number. This factor tree shows the prime factors of 20.

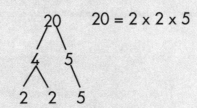

$20 = 2 \times 2 \times 5$

Use factor trees to find the prime factorization of these numbers.

4   12 = _____

18 = _____

5   40 = _____

27 = _____

Divisibility Rules

29

Divisibility Rules	
Number	**Divisible by**
even; ends in 0, 2, 4, 6, 8	2
ends in 0 or 5	5
ends in 0	10
sum of the digits is divisible by 3	3
divisible by 2 and 3	6

Note: 1 is a factor of every number. If a number is divisible by 2, then 2 is a factor of that number.

What are the factors of 36? It's even, so, it's divisible by 2. The sum of its digits is divisible by 3. Since it's divisible by 2 and 3, it's divisible by 6.

The factors of 36 are
1, 2, 3, 4, 6, 9, 12, 18, 36

1 and 36   2 and 18   3 and 12
4 and 9   6 and 6 are **factor pairs.**

Tell whether each number is divisible by 2, 3, 5, 6, or 10.

1   20 _2, 5, 10_____   27 _____

2   42 _____   56 _____

3   38 _____   70 _____

4   64 _____   90 _____

List the factors for each number in order. Think of factor pairs.

5   21 _____   30 _____

6   56 _____   42 _____

7   64 _____   80 _____

8   96 _____   100 _____

Greatest Common Factor

30

⭐ The **greatest common factor (GCF)** of two or more numbers is the greatest number that is a factor of both numbers.

<u>Find the GCF of 12 and 30.</u>
Factors of 12: ①②③ 4, ⑥ 12
Factors of 30: ①②③ 5, ⑥ 10, 15, 30
Common factors: 1, 2, 3, ⑥
Greatest common factor: **6**
The GCF of 12 and 30 is 6.

List the factors for each pair. Then circle the GCF.

1 18 _____ 24 _____
8 _____ 20 _____

2 10 _____ 25 _____
15 _____ 24 _____

3 24 _____ 40 _____
36 _____ 16 _____

Find the GCF of the numerator and denominator.

4 $\dfrac{15}{20}$ $\dfrac{18}{30}$ $\dfrac{16}{21}$ $\dfrac{12}{36}$ $\dfrac{10}{25}$

5 $\dfrac{24}{30}$ $\dfrac{8}{25}$ $\dfrac{9}{15}$ $\dfrac{14}{35}$ $\dfrac{16}{40}$

6 $\dfrac{6}{15}$ $\dfrac{12}{30}$ $\dfrac{18}{21}$ $\dfrac{5}{25}$ $\dfrac{8}{40}$

Least Common Multiple

31

⭐ The **least common multiple (LCM)** of two or more numbers is the smallest number that is a multiple of the numbers.

<u>Find the LCM of 6 and 10.</u>
Multiples of 6: 6, 12, 18, 24, ㉚, 36, ...
Multiples of 10: 10, 20, ㉚, 40, ...
Least common multiple: **30**
The LCM of 6 and 10 is 30.

List the first 10 multiples of each number. Then, circle the LCM.

1 4 _____   6 _____
    5 _____   3 _____

2 2 _____   7 _____
    9 _____   4 _____

3 8 _____   10 _____
    6 _____   8 _____

Find the LCM of each set of numbers.

4   3 and 15 _____   6 and 9 _____   8 and 12 _____

5   10 and 15 _____   6 and 7 _____   5 and 25 _____

6   9 and 12 _____   3, 4, and 6 _____   2, 5, and 9 _____

Name _____

32

The **least common denominator (LCD)** of two or more fractions is the smallest number that is a multiple of both denominators.

Find the LCD of ¼ and ⅔.
Multiples of 4: 4, 8, ⑫ 16, …
Multiples of 3: 3, 6, 9, ⑫ 15, …
Least common multiple: **12**
So the LCD of ¼ and ⅔ is 12.

List multiples of each denominator to find the LCD of each pair of fractions.

1 ¾ and ⅙

Multiples of 4: _____
Multiples of 6: _____
LCD: _____

2 ⅜ and ⁵/₁₂

Multiples of 8: _____
Multiples of 12: _____
LCD: _____

3 ⅔ and ⅗

Multiples of 3: _____
Multiples of 5: _____
LCD: _____

Find the LCD of each pair of fractions.

4 ⅔ and ⅘ _____   ⅓ and ⁷/₁₂ _____   ²/₉ and ½ _____

5 ¾ and ²/₉ _____   ¼ and ⅖ _____   ⁷/₁₀ and ³/₂₅ _____

Sequences

33

A **sequence** is a set of numbers that follows a certain pattern or rule.
The numbers in a sequence are called **terms.**
Find the pattern for this sequence. Then, write the next three terms.

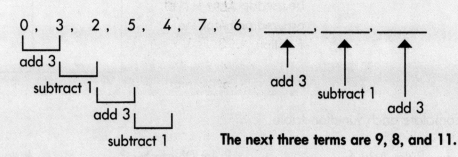

0 , 3 , 2 , 5 , 4 , 7 , 6 , _____, _____, _____

add 3

subtract 1

add 3

subtract 1

add 3

subtract 1

add 3

subtract 1

add 3

The next three terms are 9, 8, and 11.

Find the pattern for each sequence. Then, write the next three terms.

1 60, 54, 48, 42, _____, _____, _____   Pattern: _____

2 3, 6, 12, 24, 48, _____, _____, _____   Pattern: _____

3 2, 8, 32, 128, _____, _____, _____   Pattern: _____

4 5, 10, 7, 12, 9, 14, _____, _____, _____   Pattern: _____

5 4.7, 5.8, 6.9, 8, 9.1, _____, _____, _____   Pattern: _____

6 100, 90, 92, 82, 84, _____, _____, _____   Pattern: _____

7 ¼, ¾, 1¼, 1¾, _____, _____, _____   Pattern: _____

8 ½, ¼, ⅛, 1/16, _____, _____, _____   Pattern: _____

9 81, 72, 63, 54, _____, _____, _____   Pattern: _____

Name _____

34

⭐ A **function** is a relationship between two numbers and follows a **rule.** A table can be used to show sets of ordered pairs for the function.

Rule: **Multiply by 3**

Input	Output
6	18
8	24
3	9

Input
↓
← 3 x 6
← 3 x 8
← 3 x 3

Complete each function table.

1 Rule: Add 6

Input	Output
23	____
40	____
____	55

Rule: Divide by 3

Input	Output
45	____
____	8
60	____

Rule: Subtract 5

Input	Output
50	____
____	35
5	____

2 Rule: _____

Input	Output
17	21
29	33
68	72

Rule: _____

Input	Output
8	40
3	15
20	100

Rule: _____

Input	Output
24	17
35	28
91	84

⭐ When a number is multiplied by itself, the product is the **square** of the number.

$3 \times 3 = 9$ ← square number
$5 \times 5 = 25$ ←

Find the square of each number.

3 $1 \times 1 =$ ___ $2 \times 2 =$ ___ $3 \times 3 =$ ___ $4 \times 4 =$ ___ $5 \times 5 =$ ___ $6 \times 6 =$ ___

4 $7 \times 7 =$ ___ $8 \times 8 =$ ___ $9 \times 9 =$ ___ $10 \times 10 =$ ___ $11 \times 11 =$ ___ $12 \times 12 =$ ___

5 Do you see a pattern in the products 1, 4, 9, …? Explain. _____

_____

Advantage Math Grade 5 © 2004 Creative Teaching Press

Take a Test Drive

Test-Taking Tip: Read all the answer choices before choosing one.

Fill in the bubble beside the correct answer.

1 Which is a prime number?
- ○ 27
- ○ 39
- ○ 43
- ○ 51

2 Which is a composite number?
- ○ 23
- ○ 33
- ○ 43
- ○ 53

3 Which set shows **all** factors of 36?
- ○ 1, 6, 36
- ○ 1, 4, 6, 9, 36
- ○ 1, 2, 3, 4, 6, 8, 12, 18, 36
- ○ 1, 2, 3, 4, 6, 9, 12, 18, 36

4 A number that ends in 0 or 5 is divisible by _____.
- ○ 2
- ○ 3
- ○ 5
- ○ 10

5 A _____ is a number that has only two factors.
- ○ composite
- ○ even
- ○ prime
- ○ square

6 The number _____ is neither prime nor composite.
- ○ 0
- ○ 1
- ○ 2
- ○ 3

7 Which is **not** a factor pair of 48?
- ○ 3 and 16
- ○ 2 and 24
- ○ 4 and 12
- ◑ 6 and 9

8 The GCF of 18 and 30 is _____.
- ○ 2
- ○ 3
- ○ 6
- ○ 18

Name _____

Take a Test Drive

Fill in the bubble beside the correct answer.

1 The GCF of 15 and 21 is _____.
- ○ 1
- ○ 3
- ○ 7
- ○ 15

2 The LCM of 8 and 10 is _____.
- ○ 10
- ○ 20
- ○ 40
- ○ 80

3 The LCM of ⅜ and ⁵⁄₁₂ is _____.
- ○ 8
- ○ 12
- ○ 24
- ○ 96

4 The next three terms in the sequence 2, 4, 8, 16, 32 are _____.
- ○ 36, 40, 44
- ○ 40, 48, 56
- ○ 64, 96, 128
- ○ 64, 128, 256

5 What is the pattern for this sequence? 6, 10, 9, 13, 12, 16
- ○ add 4, add 1
- ○ add 4, add 3, add 7
- ○ add 4, subtract 1
- ○ add 4, divide by 2

6 Find the missing number.
- ○ 0
- ○ 6
- ○ 12
- ○ 36

Rule: Multiply by 6

Input	Output
5	30
7	42
0	

7 The GCF of 36 and 48 is _____.
- ○ 4
- ○ 6
- ○ 9
- ○ 12

8 What is the rule?
- ○ add 7
- ○ subtract 7
- ○ multiply by 7
- ○ divide by 7

Rule:

Input	Output
42	35
71	64
63	56

Fractions

37 ⭐ A **fraction** represents part of a whole or a set. In a **proper fraction,** the numerator is less than the denominator.

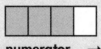   

numerator → $\dfrac{3}{4}$ = number of parts shaded
denominator   total number of parts

A **decimal** also represents part of something. A fraction or decimal can be written to represent a fractional number.

 3 tenths shaded
0.3 or ³⁄₁₀

  33 hundredths shaded
0.33 or ³³⁄₁₀₀

Write a fraction for each shaded part.

1 _____   _____   _____

2 _____   _____   _____

Write a fraction and a decimal for each shaded part.

3 _____ _____   _____ _____   _____ _____

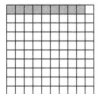

Equivalent Fractions

38

⭐ Equivalent fractions name the same amount.

$\dfrac{3}{4}$

$\dfrac{6}{8}$ $\dfrac{3}{4} \times \dfrac{2}{2} = \dfrac{6}{8}$ The same amount is shaded.

$\dfrac{9}{12}$ $\dfrac{3}{4} \times \dfrac{3}{3} = \dfrac{9}{12}$

Find the missing numerator or denominator.

1 $\dfrac{1}{2} = \dfrac{4}{8}$ $\dfrac{2}{5} = \dfrac{4}{-}$ $\dfrac{2}{3} = \dfrac{}{15}$ $\dfrac{6}{8} = \dfrac{}{4}$ $\dfrac{}{3} = \dfrac{8}{12}$ $\dfrac{1}{2} = \dfrac{}{8}$

2 $\dfrac{3}{10} = \dfrac{}{100}$ $\dfrac{15}{18} = \dfrac{5}{-}$ $\dfrac{}{12} = \dfrac{3}{4}$ $\dfrac{8}{20} = \dfrac{}{5}$ $\dfrac{5}{-} = \dfrac{15}{27}$ $\dfrac{}{49} = \dfrac{6}{7}$

3 $\dfrac{3}{4} = \dfrac{}{28}$ $\dfrac{1}{2} = \dfrac{9}{-}$ $\dfrac{2}{3} = \dfrac{}{24}$ $\dfrac{2}{5} = \dfrac{14}{-}$ $\dfrac{8}{11} = \dfrac{24}{-}$ $\dfrac{3}{-} = \dfrac{9}{48}$

Complete the pattern with equivalent fractions.

4 $\dfrac{1}{4} , \dfrac{2}{8} , \dfrac{3}{12} ,$ ____, ____, ____ $\dfrac{2}{5} , \dfrac{4}{10} , \dfrac{6}{15} ,$ ____, ____, ____

5 $\dfrac{2}{3} , \dfrac{4}{6} , \dfrac{6}{9} ,$ ____, ____, ____ $\dfrac{40}{100} , \dfrac{20}{50} , \dfrac{10}{25} ,$ ____

6 $\dfrac{1}{7} , \dfrac{2}{14} , \dfrac{3}{21} ,$ ____, ____, ____ $\dfrac{1}{6} , \dfrac{2}{12} , \dfrac{3}{18} ,$ ____, ____, ____

Fractions in Simplest Form

39

⭐ A fraction is reduced to its **simplest form** when the only common factor of its numerator and denominator is 1.

The fastest way to show a fraction in simplest form is to divide the numerator and denominator by the greatest common factor (GCF).

$$\frac{20}{36} \div \frac{4}{4} = \frac{5}{9}$$

↑

The GCF of 20 and 36 is 4.

Another way to reduce a fraction to its simplest form is to divide the numerator and denominator by the same number as many times as you can.

$$\frac{20}{36} \div \frac{2}{2} = \frac{10}{18} \qquad \frac{10}{18} \div \frac{2}{2} = \frac{5}{9}$$

↑   ↑

Even numbers.   Even numbers.
Divide by 2.   Divide by 2.

Reduce each fraction to its simplest form.

1 $\frac{6}{10} =$ ___ $\frac{8}{12} =$ ___ $\frac{8}{24} =$ ___ $\frac{12}{21} =$ ___ $\frac{25}{100} =$ ___

2 $\frac{18}{24} =$ ___ $\frac{10}{16} =$ ___ $\frac{28}{42} =$ ___ $\frac{30}{36} =$ ___ $\frac{60}{80} =$ ___

Circle the fractions in simplest form. Reduce the other fractions to their simplest form.

3 $\frac{15}{20} = \frac{3}{4}$ $\frac{18}{28} =$ ___ $\frac{15}{30} =$ ___ $\frac{15}{16} =$ ___ $\frac{15}{27} =$ ___

4 $\frac{2}{6} =$ ___ $\frac{2}{3} =$ ___ $\frac{2}{5} =$ ___ $\frac{2}{12} =$ ___ $\frac{2}{100} =$ ___

Use the clues to find each fraction.

5 My denominator is 6 more than my numerator. My simplest form is ⅖. What fraction am I? _____

Name _____

Compare and Order Fractions

40

⭐ To compare fractions, express each fraction using common denominators. Then, compare the numerators.

Compare $\frac{1}{2}$ and $\frac{3}{5}$.
The LCD of 2 and 5 is 10.
$\frac{1}{2} = \frac{5}{10}$ and $\frac{3}{5} = \frac{6}{10}$

Compare the numerators.
$5 < 6$
So, $\frac{1}{2} < \frac{3}{5}$.

Compare the fractions. Write <, =, or >.

1 $\frac{3}{4} \bigcirc \frac{16}{20}$ $\frac{3}{5} \bigcirc \frac{3}{8}$ $\frac{6}{8} \bigcirc \frac{9}{12}$

2 $\frac{5}{6} \bigcirc \frac{5}{12}$ $\frac{8}{10} \bigcirc \frac{24}{30}$ $\frac{4}{9} \bigcirc \frac{5}{12}$

3 $\frac{1}{2} \bigcirc \frac{1}{3}$ $\frac{1}{10} \bigcirc \frac{1}{4}$ $\frac{2}{3} \bigcirc \frac{2}{5}$

Order the fractions in each set from least to greatest.

4 $\frac{3}{4}, \frac{3}{8}, \frac{1}{2}$ _____ $\frac{7}{10}, \frac{1}{2}, \frac{3}{5}$ _____

5 $\frac{1}{2}, \frac{2}{3}, \frac{3}{4}$ _____ $\frac{3}{5}, \frac{7}{10}, \frac{3}{4}$ _____

---

6 Jasmine ate ¼ of the pizza. Dylan ate ⅓ of it. Who ate more? _____

7 Squirmy Worm is ⅚ inch long. Wiggly Worm is ⅞ inch long. Who is longer?

_____

Mixed Numbers and Improper Fractions

41

⭐ A **mixed number** is a whole number and a fraction. It is greater than 1.

$1\frac{2}{5}$ $2\frac{1}{5}$

An **improper fraction** is a number equal to or greater than 1. The numerator is equal to or greater than the denominator.

$\frac{6}{6}$ $\frac{12}{5}$

To write a mixed number as an improper fraction: $2 \times 4 + 3 = 11$

$2\frac{3}{4}$ $2\frac{3}{4} = \frac{11}{4}$

To write an improper fraction as a mixed number:

$\frac{10}{4}$ $4\overline{)10}$ $\;\;\underline{8}\;\;$ 2 remainder $2\frac{2}{4}$ quotient

Reduce the mixed number to its simplest form.

$2\frac{2}{4} = 2\frac{1}{2}$

Write the fractions as mixed numbers in simplest form.

1 $\dfrac{15}{6} = $ ___ $\dfrac{10}{4} = $ ___ $\dfrac{16}{12} = $ ___ $\dfrac{20}{15} = $ ___ $\dfrac{9}{2} = $ ___

2 $\dfrac{27}{6} = $ ___ $\dfrac{18}{3} = $ ___ $\dfrac{7}{5} = $ ___ $\dfrac{12}{5} = $ ___ $\dfrac{25}{3} = $ ___

Write the mixed numbers as improper fractions.

3 $4\dfrac{1}{3} = $ ___ $1\dfrac{5}{8} = $ ___ $3\dfrac{3}{5} = $ ___ $5\dfrac{2}{3} = $ ___ $10\dfrac{1}{7} = $ ___

4 $8\dfrac{1}{2} = $ ___ $2\dfrac{9}{10} = $ ___ $6\dfrac{1}{3} = $ ___ $4\dfrac{1}{5} = $ ___ $7\dfrac{9}{100} = $ ___

---

5 Gabe the chef made $10\frac{1}{2}$ sandwiches to fill the 10 lunch orders for soup and half-a-sandwich. How many sandwiches did Gabe make? _____

Compare Fractions, Decimals, and Mixed Numbers

42

⭐ To compare fractions, decimals, and mixed numbers, write all the numbers as decimals or in fraction form. Use equivalent fractions to compare. Reduce the answer to simplest form.

Compare 2.35 and $2\frac{2}{5}$.

Use decimals:

2.35 and $2\frac{2}{5} = 2\frac{40}{100} = 2.40$

Since 2.35 < 2.40,

then 2.35 < $2\frac{2}{5}$.

Use fractions:

$2.35 = 2\frac{35}{100}$ $2\frac{2}{5} = 2\frac{40}{100}$

Since $2\frac{35}{100} < 2\frac{40}{100}$,

then $2.35 < 2\frac{2}{5}$.

Complete the number sentence with <, =, or >.

1 $0.8 \bigcirc \frac{5}{6}$ $\frac{9}{25} \bigcirc 0.36$ $\frac{5}{12} \bigcirc 0.4$

2 $1\frac{3}{5} \bigcirc 1.65$ $3.2 \bigcirc 3\frac{1}{6}$ $2.85 \bigcirc 2\frac{17}{20}$

Order the numbers from least to greatest.

3 $\frac{2}{3}, 0.7, \frac{5}{8}, 0.65$ $1.64, 1\frac{7}{8}, 0.070, \frac{9}{5}$

Match the numbers to the points on the number line.

4 $1.25 = $ ___ $\frac{5}{6} = $ ___ $1.4 = $ ___ $\frac{6}{5} = $ ___

5 $\frac{15}{6} = $ ___ $2.35 = $ ___ $\frac{8}{5} = $ ___ $1\frac{3}{4} = $ ___

Estimate Fraction Sums and Differences

43

⭐ Use **benchmark fractions** and rounding to help you estimate fraction sums and differences.

Benchmark numbers
$0 \quad \dfrac{1}{4} \quad \dfrac{1}{2} \quad \dfrac{3}{4} \quad 1$

$$\frac{5}{12} + \frac{4}{5}$$
$$\downarrow \qquad \downarrow$$
$$\frac{1}{2} + 1 = 1\frac{1}{2}$$

$\dfrac{5}{12} + \dfrac{4}{5}$ is *about* $1\dfrac{1}{2}$.

Round the fractions to benchmark numbers 0, $\dfrac{1}{2}$, or 1.

1 $\dfrac{5}{8}$ ___ $\dfrac{11}{12}$ ___ $\dfrac{1}{6}$ ___ $\dfrac{5}{12}$ ___ $\dfrac{7}{9}$ ___

Circle the problems that have a sum greater than 1.

2 $\dfrac{5}{8} + \dfrac{1}{6}$ $\dfrac{11}{12} + \dfrac{7}{9}$ $\dfrac{1}{6} + \dfrac{11}{12}$ $\dfrac{5}{12} + \dfrac{1}{6}$ $\dfrac{5}{12} + \dfrac{5}{8}$

Estimate each sum and difference.

3 $\dfrac{7}{12} + \dfrac{7}{8}$ $\dfrac{9}{10} - \dfrac{2}{8}$ $\dfrac{1}{9} + \dfrac{1}{2}$

$\quad \downarrow \ \downarrow$ $\quad \downarrow \ \downarrow$ $\quad \downarrow \ \downarrow$

$\_ + \_ = \_\_\_\_$ $\_ - \_ = \_\_\_\_$ $\_ + \_ = \_\_\_\_$

4 $\dfrac{7}{12} + \dfrac{3}{8}$ _____ $\dfrac{7}{8} - \dfrac{5}{12}$ _____ $\dfrac{15}{16} - \dfrac{3}{10}$ _____

5 $\dfrac{3}{4} + \dfrac{1}{8}$ _____ $\dfrac{5}{6} + \dfrac{7}{8}$ _____ $\dfrac{11}{12} - \dfrac{3}{8}$ _____

Add and Subtract Fractions

44

⭐ When the denominators are the same, add or subtract the numerators. Then, reduce the answer.

Add: $\dfrac{5}{8} + \dfrac{7}{8}$ (Estimate: $\dfrac{1}{2} + 1 = 1\dfrac{1}{2}$)

$$\dfrac{5}{8} + \dfrac{7}{8} = 1\dfrac{1}{2} \qquad \dfrac{5}{8} + \dfrac{7}{8} = \dfrac{12}{8} \qquad \dfrac{12}{8} = 1\dfrac{4}{8} = 1\dfrac{1}{2}$$

Add or subtract. Write the answer in simplest form.

1 $\dfrac{2}{9} + \dfrac{4}{9} =$ $\qquad$ $\dfrac{5}{8} - \dfrac{2}{8} =$ $\qquad$ $\dfrac{2}{5} + \dfrac{3}{5} =$

2 $\dfrac{9}{10} + \dfrac{5}{10} =$ $\qquad$ $\dfrac{14}{15} - \dfrac{5}{15} =$ $\qquad$ $\dfrac{5}{12} + \dfrac{11}{12} =$

3 $\dfrac{13}{20} - \dfrac{5}{20} =$ $\qquad$ $\dfrac{3}{4} + \dfrac{3}{4} =$ $\qquad$ $\dfrac{15}{16} - \dfrac{7}{16} =$

4 $\dfrac{3}{8} + \dfrac{7}{8} =$ $\qquad$ $\dfrac{2}{15} + \dfrac{8}{15} =$ $\qquad$ $\dfrac{5}{12} - \dfrac{3}{12} =$

5 $2\dfrac{4}{5} + 3\dfrac{2}{5} =$ $\qquad$ $6\dfrac{7}{8} - 4\dfrac{5}{8} =$ $\qquad$ $4\dfrac{5}{6} + 1\dfrac{3}{6} =$

6 Andrea's potted daisy sprouted. It was 1¾ inches high. The next week, it grew another ¾ inch. How tall did the daisy grow? _____

7 To mow the lawn, Jimmy uses ¼ tank of gas. If Jimmy started with ¾ tank, how much gas will be left in the mower when he finishes? _____

Name _____

Add Fractions with Unlike Denominators

45 ⭐ Add: $\dfrac{3}{4} + \dfrac{7}{12}$ (Estimate: $1 + \dfrac{1}{2} = 1\dfrac{1}{2}$)

Rewrite as equivalent fractions with like denominators.

$$\frac{3}{4} + \frac{7}{12} = \frac{9}{12} + \frac{7}{12}$$

Add the numerators.

$$\frac{9}{12} + \frac{7}{12} = \frac{16}{12}$$

Write the sum in simplest form.

$$\frac{16}{12} = 1\frac{4}{12} = 1\frac{1}{3}$$

Add. Write the sum in simplest form.

1 $\dfrac{3}{4} \quad \dfrac{9}{12}$
$\dfrac{1}{3} \quad \dfrac{4}{12}$
$+\phantom{\dfrac{1}{3}} \quad +\overline{}$
$\qquad\qquad \dfrac{13}{12} = 1\frac{1}{2}$

$\dfrac{2}{5}$
$+\dfrac{3}{4}$

$\dfrac{5}{6}$
$+\dfrac{2}{3}$

2 $\dfrac{1}{6}$
$+\dfrac{1}{2}$

$\dfrac{7}{12}$
$+\dfrac{1}{4}$

$\dfrac{2}{3}$
$+\dfrac{1}{4}$

3 $\dfrac{7}{8}$
$+\dfrac{1}{3}$

$\dfrac{3}{4}$
$+\dfrac{2}{3}$

$\dfrac{7}{8}$
$+\dfrac{7}{10}$

4 $\dfrac{1}{2} + \dfrac{1}{3} + \dfrac{1}{4} =$

---

5 Jack had ¼ can of paint left from one project and ⅕ can left from another. If he combined the cans, how much paint would Jack have? _____

Name _____

46 ⭐ Subtract: $\frac{11}{12} - \frac{2}{3}$ Estimate: $1 - \frac{2}{3} = \frac{1}{3}$

Rewrite as equivalent fractions with like denominators.	Subtract the numerators.	Write the difference in simplest form.
$\frac{11}{12} - \frac{2}{3} = \frac{11}{12} - \frac{8}{12}$	$\frac{11}{12} - \frac{8}{12} = \frac{3}{12}$	$\frac{3}{12} = \frac{1}{4}$

Subtract. Write the difference in simplest form.

1
$\begin{array}{r}\frac{1}{2}\\-\frac{1}{6}\end{array}$
$\begin{array}{r}\frac{4}{5}\\-\frac{3}{10}\end{array}$
$\begin{array}{r}\frac{7}{12}\\-\frac{1}{4}\end{array}$

2
$\begin{array}{r}\frac{5}{6}\\-\frac{1}{4}\end{array}$
$\begin{array}{r}\frac{2}{3}\\-\frac{2}{5}\end{array}$
$\begin{array}{r}\frac{9}{10}\\-\frac{2}{5}\end{array}$

3
$\begin{array}{r}\frac{3}{4}\\-\frac{3}{5}\end{array}$
$\begin{array}{r}\frac{7}{8}\\-\frac{5}{6}\end{array}$
$\begin{array}{r}\frac{7}{8}\\-\frac{1}{3}\end{array}$

4 Marco the Magician had a rope $\frac{11}{12}$ of a foot long. He cut off $\frac{1}{2}$ foot. How much should there be left? _____

5 Marco used $\frac{2}{3}$ of his many rabbits during his act. If $\frac{1}{4}$ of them escaped during the trick, how many rabbits did Marco have left? _____

Estimate Mixed Number Sums and Differences

47

⭐ To estimate with mixed numbers, round mixed numbers to whole numbers.

Estimate: $2\dfrac{3}{4} + 3\dfrac{1}{5}$ $\qquad$ $2\dfrac{3}{4} + 3\dfrac{1}{5}$ is *about* 6.

$\qquad\qquad \downarrow \quad\; \downarrow$

$\qquad\qquad 3 + 3 = 6$

Round each mixed number to the nearest whole number.

1 $2\dfrac{1}{8}$ ___ $\qquad$ $4\dfrac{2}{3}$ ___ $\qquad$ $4\dfrac{1}{4}$ ___ $\qquad$ $1\dfrac{2}{9}$ ___ $\qquad$ $6\dfrac{1}{2}$ ___

Estimate each sum and difference.

2 $5\dfrac{7}{8} - 2\dfrac{1}{3}$ $\qquad\qquad$ $3\dfrac{1}{2} + 4\dfrac{3}{4}$ $\qquad\qquad$ $4\dfrac{1}{5} - \dfrac{9}{10}$

$\quad\;\; \downarrow \;\; \downarrow$ $\qquad\qquad\qquad \downarrow \;\; \downarrow$ $\qquad\qquad\qquad \downarrow \;\; \downarrow$

$\quad\;\; \_ - \_$ $\qquad\qquad\qquad \_ + \_$ $\qquad\qquad\qquad \_ - \_$

3 $\dfrac{7}{8} - \dfrac{1}{3}$ ___ $\qquad\qquad$ $12\dfrac{3}{5} - 4\dfrac{1}{3}$ ___ $\qquad\qquad$ $5\dfrac{1}{12} + 3\dfrac{3}{4}$ ___

4 $9\dfrac{1}{8} - 8\dfrac{3}{4}$ ___ $\qquad\qquad$ $5\dfrac{5}{6} + 3\dfrac{1}{9}$ ___ $\qquad\qquad$ $7\dfrac{2}{3} + 1\dfrac{7}{9}$ ___

5 $2\dfrac{1}{2} + 2\dfrac{1}{3} + 2\dfrac{1}{10}$ _____ $\qquad\qquad$ $1\dfrac{1}{2} + 2\dfrac{1}{3} + 1\dfrac{2}{3}$ _____

6 $3\dfrac{7}{8} + 4\dfrac{1}{5} + 1\dfrac{1}{2}$ _____ $\qquad\qquad$ $1\dfrac{5}{8} + 1\dfrac{1}{4} + 2\dfrac{5}{8}$ _____

Add Mixed Numbers

48

⭐ Add: $1\frac{1}{2} + 4\frac{5}{6}$ (Estimate: $2 + 5 = 7$)

Rewrite fractional parts with common denominators.

Add the fractions.
Add the whole numbers.

Write the sum in simplest form.

$$1\frac{2}{3} + 4\frac{5}{6} = 1\frac{4}{6} + 4\frac{5}{6}$$

$$1\frac{4}{6} + 4\frac{5}{6} = 5\frac{9}{6}$$

$$5\frac{9}{6} = 6\frac{3}{6} = 6\frac{1}{2}$$

Add. Write the sum in simplest form.

1. $9\frac{1}{4} + 2\frac{7}{8} =$ $3\frac{2}{9} + 5\frac{2}{3} =$ $2\frac{1}{4} + 1\frac{7}{8} =$

2. $8\frac{3}{5} + 2\frac{7}{10} =$ $2\frac{3}{4} + 1\frac{1}{3} =$ $4\frac{1}{6} + 6\frac{1}{4} =$

3. $8\frac{1}{3} + 2\frac{3}{4} =$ $4\frac{2}{3} + 1\frac{1}{4} =$ $4\frac{8}{9} + 3\frac{2}{3} =$

4. $2\frac{7}{8} + 6 + 3\frac{2}{5} =$

5. The recipe for banana bread called for 2¼ cups of white flour and 1⅔ cups of wheat flour. How much flour is needed altogether? _____

Subtract Mixed Numbers

49

⭐ Subtract: $6\frac{1}{2} - 1\frac{7}{8}$ Estimate: $7 - 2 = 5$

Rewrite fractional parts with common denominators.

$$6\frac{1}{2} - 1\frac{7}{8} = 6\frac{4}{8} - 1\frac{7}{8}$$

Subtract the fractions.
Regroup if needed.
Subtract the whole numbers.

$$6\frac{4}{8} - 1\frac{7}{8} = ? \quad 5\frac{12}{8} - 1\frac{7}{8} = 4\frac{5}{8}$$

Write the difference in simplest form.

$4\frac{5}{8}$ is in simplest form.

Rewrite each mixed number as an improper fraction.

1 $4\frac{2}{3} = 3\frac{}{3}$ $7\frac{1}{8} = 6\frac{}{8}$ $4 = 3\frac{}{8}$ $7\frac{4}{9} = 6\frac{}{9}$ $9 = \frac{}{12}$

Subtract. Write the difference in simplest form.

2 $4\frac{4}{5} - 2\frac{1}{10} =$ $4\frac{1}{6} - 1\frac{2}{3} =$ $3\frac{1}{8} - 1\frac{3}{4} =$

3 $7\frac{1}{8} - 2\frac{1}{2} =$ $5 - 3\frac{5}{8} =$ $2\frac{3}{5} - 1\frac{7}{10} =$

4 $9 - 5\frac{11}{12} =$ $9\frac{1}{2} - 3\frac{1}{3} =$ $7\frac{5}{8} - 2\frac{2}{3} =$

5 $2\frac{4}{5} - 1\frac{3}{10} =$ $3\frac{7}{8} - 2\frac{1}{4} =$ $4\frac{1}{6} - 2\frac{1}{3} =$

Name _____

Add and Subtract Fraction Practice

50

Add or subtract. Write the answer in simplest form.

1. $\dfrac{5}{8}+\dfrac{7}{8}=$ $\dfrac{5}{9}-\dfrac{1}{9}=$ $6\dfrac{3}{5}+8\dfrac{2}{5}=$

2. $\dfrac{5}{8}+\dfrac{1}{6}=$ $\dfrac{1}{2}-\dfrac{1}{9}=$ $7\dfrac{5}{12}-3\dfrac{3}{12}=$

3. $\dfrac{2}{3}+\dfrac{3}{4}=$ $\dfrac{7}{10}-\dfrac{2}{5}=$ $\dfrac{5}{6}-\dfrac{3}{4}=$

4. $3\dfrac{1}{4}+2\dfrac{7}{8}=$ $\dfrac{7}{8}-\dfrac{2}{5}=$ $2\dfrac{7}{10}-1\dfrac{1}{5}=$

5. $7-3\dfrac{3}{4}=$ $3\dfrac{1}{6}-1\dfrac{2}{3}=$ $7\dfrac{5}{8}+\dfrac{2}{3}=$

6. Morgan and Logan added ⅓ cup blueberries and ¼ cup raspberries to their muffin mix. How many cups of berries did they add altogether?

_____

Multiply Fractions

51

⭐ Multiply: $\dfrac{1}{4} \times \dfrac{8}{9}$

Multiply the numerators.	Multiply the denominators.	Write the product in simplest form.	Canceling is a shortcut.
$\dfrac{1}{4} \times \dfrac{8}{9} = \dfrac{8}{-}$	$\dfrac{1}{4} \times \dfrac{8}{9} = \dfrac{8}{36}$	$\dfrac{8}{36} \div \dfrac{4}{4} = \dfrac{2}{9}$	$\dfrac{1}{\cancel{4}_{1}} \times \dfrac{\cancel{8}^{2}}{9} = \dfrac{2}{9}$

Multiply. Write the product in simplest form.

1 $\dfrac{1}{3} \times \dfrac{1}{3} =$ $\dfrac{5}{8} \times \dfrac{2}{5} =$ $\dfrac{3}{4} \times 6 =$

2 $\dfrac{3}{8} \times \dfrac{4}{5} =$ $\dfrac{1}{2} \times \dfrac{2}{3} =$ $\dfrac{1}{8} \times \dfrac{5}{6} =$

3 $\dfrac{4}{5} \times \dfrac{1}{2} =$ $\dfrac{5}{8} \times \dfrac{3}{5} =$ $8 \times \dfrac{3}{4} =$

4 $\dfrac{3}{4} \times \dfrac{4}{9} =$ $\dfrac{5}{12} \times 4 =$ $\dfrac{2}{9} \times \dfrac{1}{2} =$

5 $\dfrac{5}{12} \times \dfrac{2}{3} =$ $\dfrac{2}{5} \times \dfrac{3}{8} =$ $\dfrac{3}{8} \times 8 =$

6 $3 \times \dfrac{4}{9} =$ $\dfrac{6}{7} \times \dfrac{3}{4} =$ $\dfrac{5}{6} \times \dfrac{3}{5} =$

Name _____

52

⭐ Subtract: $1\frac{1}{4} \times 2\frac{2}{3}$ (Estimate: 1 × 3 = 3)

Rewrite mixed numbers as improper fractions.

$1\frac{1}{4} \times 2\frac{2}{3}$ $\frac{5}{4} \times \frac{8}{3}$

Multiply the numerators.
Multiply the denominators.

$\frac{5}{4} \times \frac{8}{3} = \frac{40}{12}$

Write the product in simplest form.

$\frac{40}{12} = 3\frac{4}{12} = 3\frac{1}{3}$

Multiply. Write the product in simplest form.

1 $1\frac{1}{5} \times 1\frac{1}{4} =$ $1\frac{2}{3} \times 1\frac{1}{2} =$ $1\frac{1}{3} \times \frac{3}{4} =$

2 $3\frac{1}{3} \times 6 =$ $1\frac{1}{4} \times 1\frac{2}{3} =$ $5\frac{1}{2} \times 1\frac{1}{3} =$

3 $4 \times 1\frac{2}{3} =$ $2\frac{1}{4} \times 1\frac{2}{3} =$ $3\frac{1}{2} \times 1\frac{1}{3} =$

4 $5\frac{1}{3} \times 1\frac{3}{4} =$ $3\frac{1}{2} \times 3\frac{1}{2} =$ $15 \times 1\frac{1}{10} =$

5 $2\frac{5}{8} \times 2 =$ $3\frac{3}{5} \times 4 =$ $5\frac{1}{2} \times 1\frac{2}{3} =$

6 $4\frac{2}{7} \times 3\frac{1}{2} =$ $1\frac{1}{8} \times 5\frac{1}{2} =$ $6\frac{2}{3} \times 2\frac{3}{4} =$

Name _____

Take a Test Drive

Test-Taking Tip: Remember to reduce fractions to their simplest form.

Fill in the bubble beside the correct answer.

---

1 Which fraction names the shaded part?

○ $\frac{2}{3}$ ○ $\frac{3}{9}$

○ $\frac{3}{12}$ ○ $\frac{9}{12}$

---

2 Which fraction names the point on the number line?

0 —•— 1

○ $\frac{1}{7}$ ○ $\frac{3}{10}$

○ $\frac{7}{10}$ ○ $1\frac{3}{10}$

---

3 Which fraction is **not** equivalent to $\frac{2}{3}$?

○ $\frac{6}{9}$ ○ $\frac{9}{12}$

○ $\frac{12}{18}$ ○ $\frac{16}{24}$

---

4 Which fraction is the simplest form of $\frac{36}{48}$?

○ $\frac{2}{3}$ ○ $\frac{4}{9}$

○ $\frac{3}{4}$ ○ $\frac{9}{12}$

---

5 Which fraction is greater than $\frac{4}{5}$?

○ $\frac{2}{3}$ ○ $\frac{3}{4}$

○ $\frac{4}{3}$ ○ $\frac{5}{7}$

---

6 Which fraction is less than 0.6?

○ $\frac{1}{2}$ ○ $\frac{2}{3}$

○ $\frac{4}{5}$ ○ $\frac{6}{7}$

---

7 Which mixed number is greater than $2\frac{2}{3}$?

○ $2\frac{5}{12}$ ○ $2\frac{2}{9}$

○ $2\frac{4}{5}$ ○ $2\frac{4}{9}$

---

8 Which mixed number is equivalent to $\frac{20}{8}$?

○ $2\frac{1}{4}$ ○ $2\frac{1}{2}$

○ $2\frac{3}{4}$ ○ $2\frac{7}{8}$

54

Name _____

Take a Test Drive

Fill in the bubble beside the correct answer.

---

1 Which set is in order from least to greatest?

○ $0.7, \dfrac{2}{3}, \dfrac{5}{8}$　　○ $\dfrac{2}{3}, 0.7, \dfrac{5}{8}$

○ $\dfrac{5}{8}, \dfrac{2}{3}, 0.7$　　○ $\dfrac{2}{3}, \dfrac{5}{8}, 0.7$

---

2 Which statement is true for the numbers shown on the number line?

(number line from 0 to 2)

○ $1\dfrac{1}{6} < 1\dfrac{1}{2}$　　○ $\dfrac{5}{6} < 1.5$

○ $1\dfrac{1}{2} < \dfrac{4}{5}$　　○ $0.8 < 1\dfrac{1}{2}$

---

3 Which is a good estimate for $\dfrac{5}{12} + \dfrac{8}{9}$?

○ $\dfrac{1}{2}$　　○ 1

○ $1\dfrac{1}{2}$　　○ 2

---

4 $\dfrac{1}{4} + \dfrac{7}{12} =$

○ $\dfrac{1}{2}$　　○ $\dfrac{5}{6}$

○ $\dfrac{7}{12}$　　○ $\dfrac{8}{16}$

---

5 $\dfrac{3}{4} - \dfrac{2}{9} =$

○ $\dfrac{1}{5}$　　○ $\dfrac{7}{12}$

○ $\dfrac{19}{36}$　　○ $\dfrac{1}{12}$

---

6 $3\dfrac{1}{3} + 1\dfrac{3}{4} =$

○ $4\dfrac{1}{12}$　　○ $4\dfrac{11}{12}$

○ $5\dfrac{1}{12}$　　○ $5\dfrac{1}{6}$

---

7 $3\dfrac{1}{6} - 1\dfrac{2}{3} =$

○ $2\dfrac{1}{3}$　　○ $2\dfrac{1}{2}$

○ $2\dfrac{5}{6}$　　○ $1\dfrac{1}{2}$

---

8 $4\dfrac{1}{2} \times \dfrac{2}{3} =$

○ $2\dfrac{5}{6}$　　○ 3

○ $4\dfrac{1}{3}$　　○ $5\dfrac{1}{6}$

Percents

55

⭐ A **percent** is the relationship of a number to 100. The word "percent" means "per hundred."

26 out of 100 squares are shaded. "26 hundredths"

$\frac{26}{100}$ or 0.26 or 26%

Write a fraction "per hundred," a decimal, and a percent for the shaded part of each grid.

1

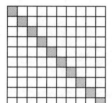

_____ , _____ , _____   _____ , _____ , _____   _____ , _____ , _____

2

   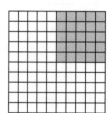

_____ , _____ , _____   _____ , _____ , _____   _____ , _____ , _____

3

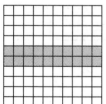   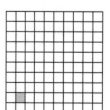

_____ , _____ , _____   _____ , _____ , _____   _____ , _____ , _____

Name _____

56

To write a percent as a fraction:

Write the percent as a fraction with a denominator of 100.
Then reduce.

$$45\% = \frac{45}{100} = \frac{9}{20}$$

To write a fraction as a percent:

Find an equivalent fraction with a denominator of 100. Write the numerator with a percent sign.

$$\frac{3}{5} \times \frac{20}{20} = \frac{60}{100} = 60\%$$

Write each percent as a fraction in simplest form.

1   20% = _____   25% = _____   10% = _____   75% = _____

2   30% = _____   50% = _____   2% = _____   36% = _____

Write each fraction as a percent.

3 $\frac{1}{4}$ = _____ $\frac{3}{5}$ = _____ $\frac{7}{20}$ = _____ $\frac{9}{10}$ = _____

4 $\frac{3}{4}$ = _____ $\frac{6}{25}$ = _____ $\frac{9}{100}$ = _____ $\frac{5}{5}$ = _____

Complete the tables.

5

fraction	decimal	percent
_____	_____	40%
_____	0.35	_____
$\frac{3}{20}$	_____	_____

fraction	decimal	percent
_____	0.08	_____
$\frac{3}{25}$	_____	_____
_____	_____	16%

Compare and Order Fractional Numbers

57

⭐ To compare fractions, decimals, and percents, write them in the same form (fractions, decimals, or percents).

Compare $\frac{3}{4}$, 0.8, and 70%.

Fractions:

$\frac{3}{4} = \frac{75}{100}$ $0.8 = \frac{8}{10} = \frac{80}{100}$ $70\% = \frac{70}{100}$

Since $\frac{7}{10} < \frac{75}{100} < \frac{80}{100}$,

then $70\% < \frac{3}{4} < 0.8$.

Decimals:

$\frac{3}{4} = \frac{75}{100} = 0.75$ $0.8 = 0.80$

$70\% = \frac{70}{100} = 0.70$

Since $0.70 < 0.75 < 0.80$,
then $70\% < \frac{3}{4} < 0.8$.

Percents:

$\frac{3}{4} = \frac{75}{100} = 75\%$

$0.8 = \frac{8}{10} = \frac{80}{100} = 80\%$

Since $70\% < 75\% < 80\%$,
then $70\% < \frac{3}{4} < 0.8$.

Complete the number sentence with <, =, or >.

1 $\frac{7}{25} \bigcirc 28\%$ $\qquad$ $0.8 \bigcirc \frac{3}{4}$ $\qquad$ $76\% \bigcirc 0.08$

2 $6\% \bigcirc \frac{3}{5}$ $\qquad$ $0.2 \bigcirc 2\%$ $\qquad$ $\frac{7}{50} \bigcirc 0.14$

3 $\frac{9}{10} \bigcirc 100\%$ $\qquad$ $25\% \bigcirc \frac{4}{12}$ $\qquad$ $16\% \bigcirc 1.6$

4 $4\% \bigcirc 0.4$ $\qquad$ $0.35 \bigcirc \frac{7}{25}$ $\qquad$ $\frac{9}{10} \bigcirc 95\%$

Order the numbers from least to greatest.

5 7%, 0.7, $\frac{7}{20}$ $\qquad$ _____

6 $\frac{9}{20}$, 3.6, 36% $\qquad$ _____

7 0.09, $\frac{9}{10}$, 99% $\qquad$ _____

Name _____

Find Percent of a Number

58

⭐ To find a percent of a number, multiply. You can use a fraction or a decimal for the percent.

Find 40% of 75.

Use a fraction for the percent:

$$40\% = \frac{40}{100} = \frac{2}{5}$$

$$\frac{2}{5} \times 75 = \frac{150}{5} = \mathbf{30}$$

40% of 75 is 30.

Use a decimal for the percent:

$$40\% = 0.40 = 0.4$$

$$75 \times 0.4 = 30.0 = \mathbf{30}$$

40% of 75 is 30.

Solve.

1   50% of 78 = _____   30% of 80 = _____   25% of 8 = _____

2   8% of 300 = _____   75% of 120 = _____   32% of 200 = _____

3   20% of 45 = _____   56% of 250 = _____   40% of 200 = _____

---

4   During basketball practice, Vanessa made 20% of the shots she threw. If she threw the ball 10 times, how many shots went in the basket? _____

5   Vanessa's team made 30% of the baskets they attempted. If the team attempted a basket 40 times, how many did they make? _____

6   The chicken pox went around Mr. Cho's class. Of 28 students, 25% got sick. How many students got sick? _____

7   Of the 30 students in Ms. Kelly's class, 40% got the chicken pox. How many students got sick? _____

Outcomes

59

 An **outcome** is a result of an experiment. It is one possible way something can happen in a probability situation.

A **sample space** is a list of all possible outcomes of an experiment.

Each outcome on this spinner is **equally likely** to happen. Sometimes an outcome is **less likely** or **more likely** to happen for an experiment.

One possible outcome is 4. The sample space is 1, 2, 3, 4, 5, 6.

List all possible outcomes for each experiment. Then, write **less, equally,** or **more** in the blank.

1

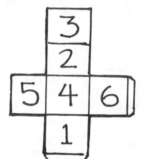

A 5 is _____ likely to happen.   An E is _____ likely to happen.

2

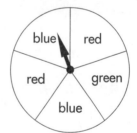

A polka-dotted ball is _____ likely to be chosen.   The arrow is _____ likely to land on green.

3

A 7 is _____ likely to happen.   A triangle is _____ likely to be chosen.

Name _____

Probability

60

⭐ A **probability** tells the likelihood that an event will happen.
The probability of an event is usually expressed as a fraction.

$$\text{Probability (event)} = \frac{\text{number of favorable outcomes}}{\text{number of all possible outcomes}}$$

$P(2) = \dfrac{1}{6}$ $\quad\quad P(n > 3) = \dfrac{3}{6} = \dfrac{1}{2}$ $\quad\quad P(1, 2, 3, 4, 5, 6) = \dfrac{6}{6} = 1$ $\quad\quad P(8) = \dfrac{0}{6} = 0$

$\quad\quad\quad\quad\quad\quad\quad\quad\quad\quad\quad\quad\quad$ **certain** $\quad\quad\quad\quad\quad\quad\quad\quad\quad$ **impossible**

Express each probability in its simplest form.

1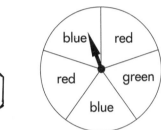

P(3) = _____
P(n < 4) = _____
P(even number) = _____

P(green) = _____
P(blue) = _____
P(blue or red) = _____

2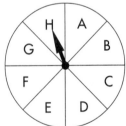

P(vowel) = _____
P(G or H) = _____
P(K) = _____

P(hexagon) = _____
P(triangle) = _____
P(not a rectangle) = _____

3 There were 2 green marbles, 2 red marbles, and 1 blue marble in a bag. If Kim pulled out 1 marble without looking, how likely would the marble be a red marble? _____

4 How likely would it be that Kim would pull out a yellow marble? _____

Range, Mode, and Median

61

⭐ Find the range, mode, and median of 12, 9, 10, 11, 12, 7, and 9.

The **range** is the difference between the greatest and least numbers of a set of data.	Range: $12 - 7 = 5$
The **mode** is the number that appears most often. There may be more than one mode. Sometimes there is no mode.	Modes: **9** and **12**
The **median** is the middle number of a set of data when listed from least to greatest.	Median: **10** 7, 9, 9, 10, 11, 12, 12 middle number

Find the range, mode, and median for each set of data.

1 12, 15, 10, 13, 12
Range: _____
Mode: _____
Median: _____

40, 50, 45, 40, 35
Range: _____
Mode: _____
Median: _____

2 40, 70, 68, 60, 72, 71, 66
Range: _____
Mode: _____
Median: _____

85, 90, 100, 88, 100, 95, 100
Range: _____
Mode: _____
Median: _____

3 115, 132, 117, 103, 121, 119, 128
Range: _____
Mode: _____
Median: _____

20, 23, 21, 20, 21
Range: _____
Mode: _____
Median: _____

4 The Gomez family played miniature golf one night. Their scores were 72, 79, 84, and 88. What is the mode? _____

5 Last week their miniature golf scores were 74, 80, 85, and 74. What is the mode? _____

Find the Mean

62

⭐ The **mean** is the average of a set of numbers.

Find the mean of
40, 50, 45, 38, and 35.

The mean is 42.

Note: A mean can be
a decimal number.

Add the numbers.	Divide by the number of addends.
40	41.6
50	5)208
45	−20
38	08
+35	−5
‾‾‾	30
208	−30
	0

Find the mean of each set of data.

1 20, 23, 21, 20, 21
Mean: _____

12, 15, 10, 13, 12, 11, 11
Mean: _____

70, 52, 64, 88
Mean: _____

2 80, 70, 68, 60, 72, 71, 61
Mean: _____

85, 90, 100, 88, 100, 95, 100, 82
Mean: _____

Find the missing number for each set of data.

3 The mean of four numbers is 83. If three of the numbers are 82, 75, and 85,
what is the fourth number? _____

4 The mean of five numbers is 28. Two of the numbers are the same. If three of the
numbers are 20, 25, and 35, what are the other two numbers? _____

5 Jared scored 75, 95, 86, and 88 on his spelling quizzes. What is his mean
score? _____

6 If Jared had scored 92 instead of 88 on his last quiz, by how many points would
his mean score have increased? _____

Line Plots

63

⭐ A **line plot** shows data by making X's above a number line. You can quickly see the range and mode.

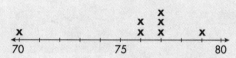

Remember:
Mode – most
Median – middle
Mean – add and divide
Range – subtract

Range: **79 – 70 = 9**
Mode: **77**
Median: **77**
Mean: **(70 + 76 + 76 + 77 + 77 + 77 + 79) = 532 ÷ 7 = 76**

Find the range, mode, median, and mean for the set of data shown on each line plot.

1

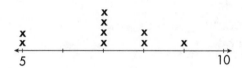

Range: _____   Mode: _____
Median: _____   Mean: _____

Range: _____   Mode: _____
Median: _____   Mean: _____

2

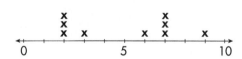

Range: _____   Mode: _____
Median: _____   Mean: _____

Range: _____   Mode: _____
Median: _____   Mean: _____

Stem-and-Leaf Graphs

64

⭐ In a **stem-and-leaf graph,** data are organized from least to greatest by their front digits. You can quickly find the range, mode, and median.

Data: 31, 33, 42, 29, 32, 23, 46, 38, 32

Stems	Leaves
2	3 9
3	1 2 2 3 8
4	2 6

Range: **46 − 23 = 23**
Mode: **32**
Median: **32**
Mean: **306 ÷ 9 = 34**

Find the range, mode, median, and mean for the data shown in each stem-and-leaf graph.

1

Stems	Leaves
6	4 9
7	3 6 7 7
8	2

Range: _____
Mode: _____
Median: _____
Mean: _____

Stems	Leaves
7	9
8	2 8 8
9	2 2 5 5 8

Range: _____
Mode: _____
Median: _____
Mean: _____

Complete the stem-and-leaf graph. Find the range, mode, median, and mean of the data.

2 Data:
26, 33, 43, 25, 35, 46, 37, 31, 28

Stems	Leaves

Range: _____
Mode: _____
Median: _____
Mean: _____

3 Data:
55, 42, 46, 55, 43, 61, 61, 62, 63

Stems	Leaves

Range: _____
Mode: _____
Median: _____
Mean: _____

4 Data:
22, 24, 17, 15, 26, 31, 31, 17, 15

Stems	Leaves

Range: _____
Mode: _____
Median: _____
Mean: _____

Bar Graphs

65

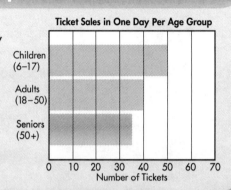

⭐ A **bar graph** uses bars to show how much or how many. They may be horizontal or vertical.

How many adult tickets were sold?
40

Top Speeds of Animals

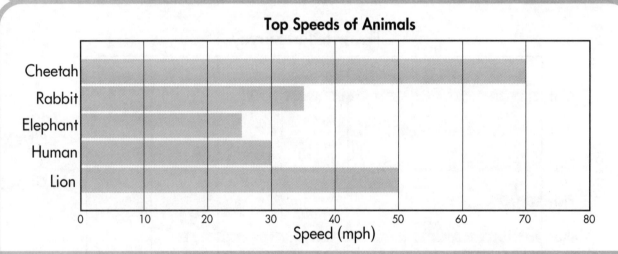

Answer the questions using the bar graph.

1 What is the speed of the lion? _____

2 What is the speed of the elephant? _____

3 Which animal is the fastest? _____

4 Which animal is twice as fast as the elephant? _____

5 Which animal is only half as fast as the cheetah? _____

6 Which animal is slower than a human? _____

7 About how much faster is a cheetah than a human? _____

Double Bar Graphs

66

⭐ Compare two different groups at the same time with a **double bar graph.**

How many boys are in Grade 6? **55**

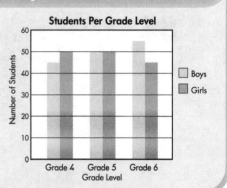

Students Per Grade Level

Boys
Girls

Favorite Pet Survey

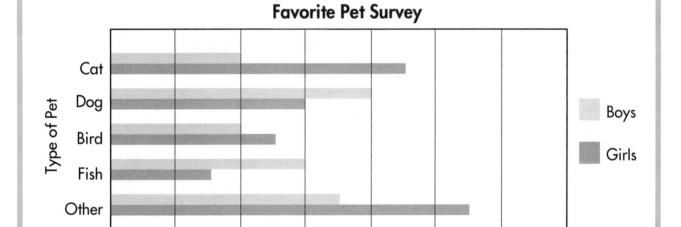

Boys

Girls

Answer the questions using the double bar graph.

1 How many boys like dogs best? _____

2 How many girls like fish best? _____

3 How many boys and girls like cats? _____

4 How many more boys than girls like dogs? _____

5 Which animal do boys like best? _____

Name _____

67

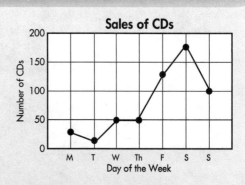

⭐ A **line graph** shows change over a period of time.

How many CDs were sold on Friday? **125**

Grade 5 Class Attendance in One Week

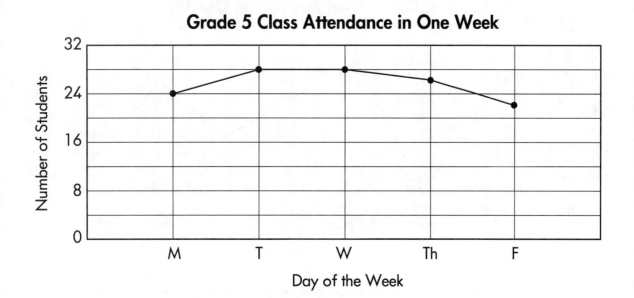

Answer the questions using the line graph.

1 How many students were in class on Tuesday? _____

2 How many students were in class on Friday? _____

3 How many more students were in class on Tuesday than on Monday? _____

4 On which days was the attendance the same? _____, _____

5 Which day had the lowest attendance? _____

Name _____

68

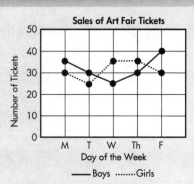

⭐ A **double line graph** shows two sets of data on the same graph.

About how many more tickets did the girls sell than the boys on Wednesday?
10

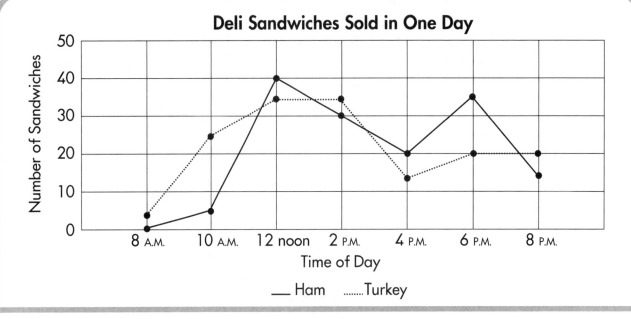

Deli Sandwiches Sold in One Day

__ Ham   ....Turkey

Answer the questions using the double line graph.

1 How many ham sandwiches were sold at 2 P.M.? _____

2 How many turkey sandwiches were sold at 6 P.M.? _____

3 When were the most sandwiches sold? _____

4 When was the greatest increase in ham sandwich sales? _____

5 About how many more turkey sandwiches than ham sandwiches were sold at 10 A.M.? _____

Name _____

Circle Graphs

69

⭐ A **circle graph** shows how parts of something are related to the whole.

If there are 24 hours in a day, what fraction of the day does Jason spend in school?

8/24 = 1/3 or 33%

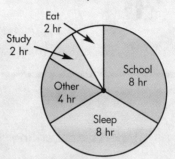

How Jason Spends His School Day

Eat 2 hr
Study 2 hr
Other 4 hr
School 8 hr
Sleep 8 hr

Hair Color of Students in a School

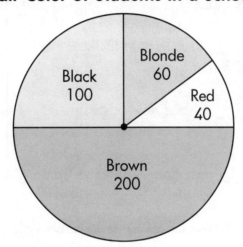

Black 100
Blonde 60
Red 40
Brown 200

Answer the questions using the circle graph.

1 How many students have black hair? _____

2 How many students are in this school? _____

3 What fraction of the students have black hair? _____

4 What percent of the students have brown hair? _____

5 What fraction of the students have red hair? _____

6 What percent of the students do not have black hair? _____

Choose Appropriate Graphs

70

Fill in the blanks.

1. A _____ shows data using X's above a number line.

2. A _____ shows change over a period of time for two things.

3. A _____ uses bars to tell how much or how many for two different groups.

4. A _____ shows how parts are related to the whole.

5. A _____ has data organized from least to greatest using front digits.

Types of Graphs
bar graph
double bar graph
circle graph
line graph
double line graph
line plot
stem-and-leaf graph

Choose the appropriate graph.

6. Show sales of backpacks in a year _____

7. Show how number of hours of sleep relates to the whole day _____

8. Compare number of boys and girls in grade levels _____

9. Organize test scores to quickly see the range, mode, and median

   _____

10. Show visitors at the zoo by children and adults in a week

    _____

Take a Test Drive

Test-Taking Tip: Read carefully the title and headings in charts and diagrams.

Fill in the bubble beside the correct answer.

1 What percent is the shaded part?

○ 25%
○ 35%
○ 65%
○ 75%

5 Which number is greater than 60%?

○ $\frac{1}{2}$ ○ 0.58

○ $\frac{11}{20}$ ○ $\frac{4}{5}$

2 What is 40% in simplest form?

○ $\frac{4}{100}$ ○ $\frac{2}{50}$

○ $\frac{4}{6}$ ○ $\frac{2}{5}$

6 Which set of numbers is in order from least to greatest?

○ 9%, 0.9, ⁹⁄₂₀   ○ 0.9, 9%, ⁹⁄₂₀

○ 9%, ⁹⁄₂₀, 0.9   ○ ⁹⁄₂₀, 0.9, 9%

3 What is ⁹⁄₂₀ expressed as a percent?

○ 9%
○ 18%
○ 36%
○ 45%

7 What is 30% of 40?

○ 70
○ 30
○ 12
○ 10

4 What is 8% expressed as a decimal?

○ 8.0
○ 0.8
○ 0.08
○ 0.008

8 What is the probability of getting an odd number?

○ $\frac{1}{8}$ ○ $\frac{1}{4}$

○ $\frac{3}{8}$ ○ $\frac{1}{2}$

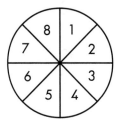

Name _____

Take a Test Drive

Fill in the bubble beside the correct answer.

1 The ____ is the middle number of a set of data listed from least to greatest.
- ○ mode
- ○ median
- ○ mean
- ○ range

2 What is the range of the data in this graph?
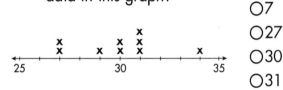
- ○ 7
- ○ 27
- ○ 30
- ○ 31

3 What is the median of the data?
- ○ 47
- ○ 52
- ○ 55
- ○ 64

Stems	Leaves
4	7 7
5	2 5
6	4

4 What is the mean of the data?
- ○ 47
- ○ 52
- ○ 53
- ○ 55

Stems	Leaves
4	7 7
5	2 5
6	4

5 How many girls are in grade 6?
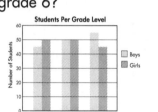
- ○ 40
- ○ 45
- ○ 50
- ○ 55

6 How many tickets did the boys sell on Wednesday?

- ○ 25
- ○ 30
- ○ 35
- ○ 40

7 What percent of the day is spent in school and on other things?
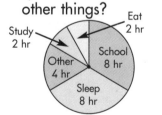
- ○ 25%
- ○ 30%
- ○ 40%
- ○ 50%

8 Which graph is the best to show the number of CDs sold in a month?
- ○ bar graph
- ○ circle graph
- ○ line graph
- ○ line plot

Geometric Ideas

73

Point	Line	Line segment
● A Point A	B A $\overleftrightarrow{AB}$	B A $\overline{AB}$

Ray	Angle	Plane
B A $\overrightarrow{AB}$	A B C ∠ABC	●A ●C ●B plane ABC

Parallel lines	Perpendicular lines	Intersecting lines
B A D C $\overleftrightarrow{AB} \parallel \overleftrightarrow{CD}$	E A B F $\overleftrightarrow{AB} \perp \overleftrightarrow{EF}$	F A B E $\overleftrightarrow{AB} \cap \overleftrightarrow{EF}$

Draw and label each figure.

1 $\overline{PQ}$ ∠PQR $\overleftrightarrow{ST}$

2 $\overleftrightarrow{WX} \cap \overleftrightarrow{YZ}$ $\overrightarrow{TV}$ $\overleftrightarrow{ST} \perp \overleftrightarrow{RQ}$

Use the figure at the right to answer the questions. Write letters and symbols to describe each geometric idea.

3 Name four lines. ____, ____, ____, ____

4 Name a ray. _____

5 Name a pair of parallel lines. _____, _____

6 Name a pair of perpendicular lines. _____, _____

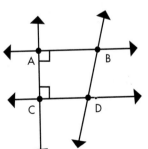

Plane and Solid Figures

74

⭐ A **polygon** is a closed figure made of line segments.

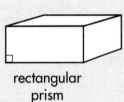

triangle   square   rectangle   rhombus   parallelogram   quadrilateral

A solid figure is a 3-dimensional closed figure. Some faces are polygons.

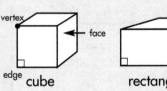

vertex ← face

edge   cube   rectangular   triangular   cylinder   cone   sphere
                    prism   prism

Fill in the blanks.

      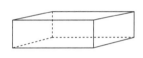

This is a _____.   This is a _____.   This is a _____.
Each face is a _____.   Each face is a _____.   Each face is a _____.
There are _____ vertices.   There are _____   Some faces are _____.
                               edges.

Write **yes** or **no** in the appropriate boxes of the chart.

Quadrilateral	Pairs of Parallel Lines	Has Right Angles	Has Equal Sides
Parallelogram			
Rhombus			
Rectangle			
Square			

Classify Angles

75

⭐ An angle is measured in **degrees.** Use a **protractor** to measure angles. A **right angle** has a measure of 90°.

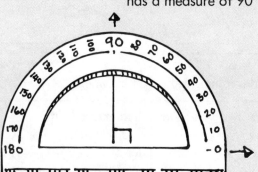

Right angle: 90°	
Acute angle: less than 90°	
Obtuse angle: greater than 90°	
Straight angle: 180°	

Write the name of the angle. Then write **less than, greater than,** or **equal to** in the blank.

1

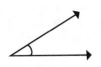

_____ angle
It is _____ 90°.

_____ angle
It is _____ 90°.

_____ angle
It is _____ 90°.

Use the diagram to answer the questions. Label each angle using three letters.

2 Name two acute angles. _____, _____

3 Name two obtuse angles. _____, _____

4 Name two right angles. _____, _____

5 Name two straight angles. _____, _____

6 What kind of angle will be formed by $\overleftrightarrow{AD}$ and $\overleftrightarrow{EH}$ if they are extended? _____

Classify Triangles

76

⭐ Triangles can be classified by the measure of their angles.

Right: one right angle 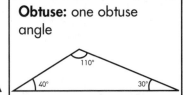	**Acute:** all acute angles 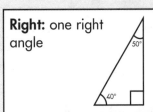	**Obtuse:** one obtuse angle 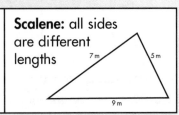

Triangles can be classified by the lengths of their sides.

Equilateral: all sides the same length 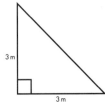	**Isosceles:** two sides the same length 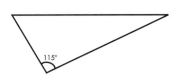	**Scalene:** all sides are different lengths 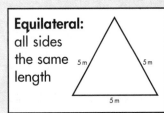

Describe each triangle using two words from the charts above.

1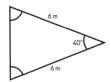

_____   _____   _____

_____   _____   _____

The sum of the measures of all the angles of any triangle is 180°. Find the missing number of degrees for the third angle of each triangle.

2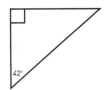

_____   _____   _____   _____

Coordinate Geometry

77

⭐ An **ordered pair** tells the location of a point.

Point A is at (4, 2).
Point B is at (2, 4).

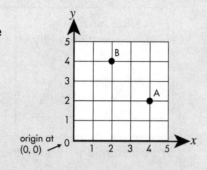

origin at
(0, 0) ➚

Remember: (across, up)

Name the ordered pair for each point.

1 A _____ B _____

C _____ D _____

E _____ F _____

G _____ H _____

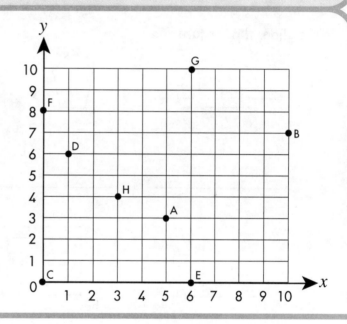

Graph each ordered pair and label it with its letter.

2 J (5, 3) K (0, 4)

L (6, 0) M (0, 0)

N (9, 1) P (4, 4)

Q (7, 3) R (10, 10)

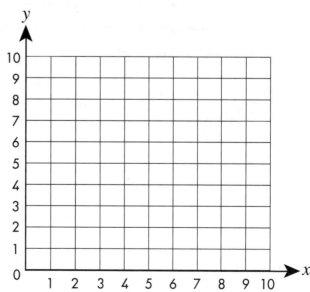

Slides, Flips, and Turns

78

A **slide** moves up, down, or diagonally.	A **flip** produces a mirror image.	A **turn** rotates around a point.
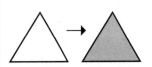	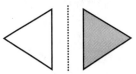	

Transformations change the positions of the figures but not their shapes.

Write **slide, flip,** or **turn.**

 1
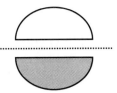   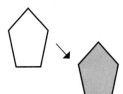

_____   _____   _____

2
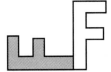

_____   _____   _____

Draw the figure after the move.

 3   flip A   turn H   slide J

4   turn   flip C   slide ◿

Similar and Congruent Figures

79

Similar figures	Congruent figures
Same shape. Different size.	Same shape. Same size.

Tell whether the figures are **similar**, **congruent**, or **neither**.

1

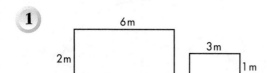

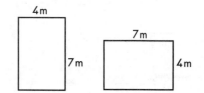

_____   _____

2

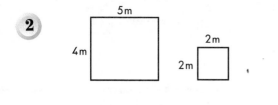

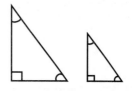

_____   _____

Circle the figure that is always similar. Explain your answer.

3

_____

_____

Circles

80

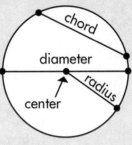

A **chord** is a line segment with endpoints on the **circle.**

A **diameter** is a chord that goes through the center of the circle.

The **radius** is a line segment from the center of the circle to a point on the circle.

diameter = 2 radii

Name the part.

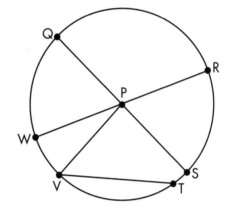

1 center _____

2 two diameters _____, _____

3 one chord _____

4 three radii _____, _____, _____

Draw the part of the circle and label the point.

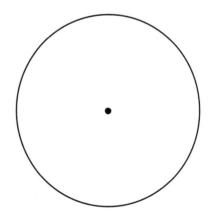

5 center X

6 diameter $\overline{WXY}$

7 radius $\overline{XZ}$

8 chord $\overline{ZT}$

Take a Test Drive

Test-Taking Tip: Examine the diagram or figure before you answer the question.

Fill in the bubble beside the correct answer.

1 This pair of lines is ____.
- ○ parallel
- ○ perpendicular
- ○ right
- ○ scalene

2 In this figure, AB is a(n) ____.
- ○ angle
- ○ line segment
- ○ line
- ○ ray

3 This figure is a ____.
One face is a ____.
- ○ pyramid, square
- ○ cube, rhombus
- ○ prism, rectangle
- ○ cube, square

4 A ____ has rectangles for all its faces.
- ○ cube
- ○ parallelogram
- ○ rectangular pyramid
- ○ rectangular prism

5 This figure is a(n) ____ angle.
- ○ acute
- ○ right
- ○ obtuse
- ○ straight

6 An angle that measures less than 90°
is a(n) ____ angle.
- ○ acute
- ○ right
- ○ obtuse
- ○ straight

7 This triangle is ____ and ____.
- ○ right, isosceles
- ○ right, scalene
- ○ acute, right
- ○ acute, scalene

8 A triangle cannot be ____ and ____.
- ○ acute, scalene
- ○ acute, isosceles
- ○ equilateral, right
- ○ equilateral, acute

Name _____

Take a Test Drive

Fill in the bubble beside the correct answer.

Use the figure to answer questions 1 and 2.

1 Point A is at ____.
- ○ (6, 3)
- ○ (6, 0)
- ○ (3, 6)
- ○ (3, 4)

2 Point ____ is at (0, 5).
- ○ B
- ○ D
- ○ E
- ○ F

3 The move made by this figure is a __.
- ○ flip
- ○ slide
- ○ turn
- ○ intersect

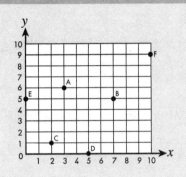

4 Which shape shows a flip of this figure?

○   ○   ○   ○

5 These two figures are ____.
- ○ congruent
- ○ slide
- ○ scalene
- ○ similar

6 Which figure is **not** congruent to this one?

○   ○   ○   ○

7 A radius is _____.
- ○ $\overline{AC}$
- ○ $\overline{AD}$
- ○ $\overline{DE}$
- ○ $\overline{AB}$

Standard Units of Length

83

1 foot (ft) = 12 inches (in.)	1 yard (yd) = 3 feet	1 mile (mi) = 5,280 feet

⭐ **To convert measurements:**
From larger to smaller units
8 yd = ___?___ ft
8 x 3 = **24 ft**

From smaller to larger units:
50 in. = ___?___ ft

4 ft 2 in. or
4⅙ ft

$$12\overline{)50} \quad \begin{array}{r} 4 \\ -48 \\ \hline 2 \end{array}$$

⭐ **To add or subtract measurements:**
Add   3 ft 9 in.
+2 ft 8 in.
5 ft 17 in. **= 6 ft 5 in.**

Subtract   4 yd   3 yd 3 ft
−2 yd 1 ft   −2 yd 1 ft
1 yd 2 ft

Complete each conversion.

1 5 ft = _____ in.   15 ft = _____ yd   96 in. = _____ ft

2 3 mi = _____ ft   4 ft 5 in. = _____ in.   70 in. = _____ ft
_____ in.

3 40 in. = _____ ft   1 mi = _____ yd   48 in. = _____ yd

Add or subtract.

4
3 yd 2 ft
+5 yd 1 ft

8 yd 1 ft
−5 yd 2 ft

4 mi
−1 mi 2,700 ft

4 yd 2 ft 8 in.
2 yd 1 ft 3 in.
+5 yd 2 ft 9 in.

---

5 Kevin is 56 inches tall. Kevin's father is 6 feet 3 inches tall. How much taller is Kevin's father than Kevin? _____

Metric Units of Length

84

 The **meter (m)** is the basic unit of length in the metric system. Units of length include the **millimeter (mm)**, **centimeter (cm)**, and **kilometer (km)**.

To convert measurements:

From larger to smaller units
25 cm = ___?___ mm
25 x 10 = 250 mm

From smaller to larger units
3,700 m = ___?___ km
3,700 ÷ 1,000 = 37 km

Metric Units of Length		
1 cm	=	10 mm
1 m	=	100 cm
1 km	=	1,000 m

Complete each conversion.

1 35 cm = _____ mm   150 cm = _____ m   2.3 km = _____ m

2 2,050 m = _____ km   370 mm = _____ cm   3.1 m = _____ cm

3 650 m = _____ km   3.5 mm = _____ cm   5 m = _____ mm

Write **mm, cm, m,** or **km** in the blank.

4 A car is about 6 _____ long.

5 A baseball bat is about 95 _____ long.

6 The distance from Dallas to Boston is about 2,500 _____.

7 The height of a man is about 2 _____.

8 A large paper clip is about 8 _____ wide.

9 A sheet of paper is about 28 _____ long and 21 _____ wide.

10 An inch is about 2.5 _____ long.

Standard Units of Weight and Capacity

85

Standard Units of Weight
1 pound (lb) = 16 ounces (oz)
1 ton (T) = 2,000 pounds

Standard Units of Capacity
1 cup (c) = 8 fluid ounces (fl oz)
1 pint (pt) = 2 cups
1 quart (qt) = 2 pints
1 gallon (gal) = 4 quarts

Complete each conversion.

1 48 oz = _____ lbs   6 T = _____ lbs   96 oz = _____ lbs

2 2.5 T = _____ lbs   12 oz = _____ lb   3,500 lb = _____ T

3 3 gal = _____ qt   6 qt = _____ pt   96 oz = _____ c

4 12 pt = _____ c   10 qt = _____ gal   3½ gal = _____ qt

5 20 fl oz = _____ c   2 pt 1 c = _____ fl oz   8 qt = _____ c

6 12 oz = _____ c   16 oz = _____ pt   ¾ gal = _____ qt

7 16 pt = _____ gal   ½ T = _____ lbs   32 oz = _____ qt

8 Megan's cat weighs 8 pounds. Maria's cat weighs 120 ounces. Whose cat weighs more? _____

9 Ben uses 50 quarts of water to fill his fish tank. Luis uses 15 gallons to fill his fish tank. Who uses more water? _____

Metric Units of Weight and Capacity

86

Metric Units of Weight	Metric Units of Capacity
1 gram (g) = 1,000 milligrams (mg)	1 liter (L) = 1,000 milliliters (mL)
1 kilogram (kg) = 1,000 grams	

Complete each conversion.

1. 8 g = _____ mg   5 kg = _____ g   4,800 mg = _____ g

2. 750 mg = _____ g   0.3 g = _____ mg   6½ kg = _____ g

3. 2 L = _____ mL   6,900 mL = _____ L   3.5 L = _____ mL

4. 370 mL = _____ L   0.09 L = _____ mL   5 mL = _____ L

Write **mg, g, kg, L,** or **mL** in the blank.

5. A glass of milk is about 250 _____.

6. An aquarium holds about 40 _____.

7. A man weighs about 80 _____.

8. A can of soup weighs about 300 _____.

9. A handful of small paper clips weighs about 50 _____.

10. An aspirin weighs about 300 _____.

Name _____

Temperature

87

⭐ Temperature is measured in **degrees.** A **thermometer** measures coldness and warmth. In the standard system, the **Fahrenheit** scale is used. In the metric system, the **Celsius** scale is used.

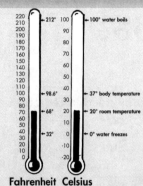

Fahrenheit Celsius

Use the Fahrenheit and Celsius thermometers to match the item to the correct temperature.

1   cool glass of milk   15°F

    lukewarm water   38°F

    human fever   90°F

    ice skating rink   103°F

2   cool glass of juice   0°C

    bath water   10°C

    ice cube   20°C

    room temperature   30°C

List an activity you would do and the clothes you would wear for each temperature.

3   −5°F _____, _____

4   −5°C _____, _____

5   30°F _____, _____

6   30°C _____, _____

Name _____

88

1 minute (min) = 60 seconds (sec)	1 week (wk) = 7 days
1 hour (h) = 60 minutes	1 year (yr) = 52 weeks
1 day (d) = 24 hours	1 year = 12 months (mo)

You may need to regroup units when you add or subtract.

```
  2h 45min          5d    →  4d 24h
 +4h 20min        −2d 18h  −2d 18h
  ───────          ───────  ───────
  6h 65min                  2d  6h
      ↘
     7h 5min
```

You can add or subtract to find elapsed time.

Start: 10:30 A.M.   Start: 2:15 P.M.
Stop: 3 h 20 min   Stop: 5:00 P.M.

```
  10:30                    5:00  →  4:60
 + 3:20                   −2:15    −2:15
  ──────                   ─────    ─────
  13:50 → 1:50 P.M.                 2:45
```

2 h 45 min

Add or subtract.

1

```
    3h 45min        4yr  6wk        7min  5sec        3h 45min
   +1h 25min       −1yr 18wk       −3min 30sec        2h 10min
                                                     +4h  5min
```

Find the elapsed time.

2   1:30 A.M. to 6:15 P.M. _____   8:30 A.M. to 3:15 P.M. _____

12 noon to 7:15 P.M. _____   10:00 P.M. to 6:30 A.M. _____

Find the starting or stopping time.

3   35 min after 2:45 P.M. _____   1 h 45 min after 9:30 A.M. _____

2 h 15 min before 7:30 P.M. _____   55 min before midnight _____

---

4   Jon started reading at 8:30. He stopped at 9:05. How long did Jon read? _____

Perimeter

89

⭐ The **perimeter** is the distance around a figure. To find the perimeter, add the lengths of all the sides.

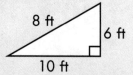

$P = 10 + 8 + 6 = 24$ ft

Find the perimeter.

1   P = _____

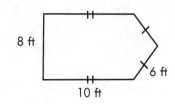

P = _____

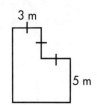

P = _____

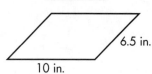

2   P = _____

P = _____

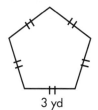

P = _____

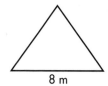

⭐ All the sides of a regular polygon are the same length. To find its perimeter, multiply the number of sides (n) times the length of one of its sides (s).

$P = n \times s = 6 \times 5 = 30$ m

Find the perimeter of each regular polygon.

3

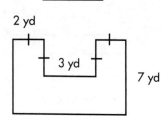

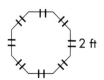

_____ _____ _____ _____

Name _____

90

Perimeter of a Square

5 cm

P = 4 sides
P = 4s
P = 4 x 5 = 20
The perimeter is 20 cm.

Perimeter of a Rectangle

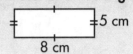
5 cm

8 cm

P = 2 lengths + 2 widths
P = 2l + 2w
P = (2 x 8) + (2 x 5)
P = 16 + 10 = 26
The perimeter is 26 cm.

Find the perimeter.

1 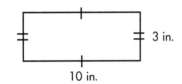 3 in.

10 in.

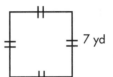 7 yd

P = 2l + 2w
P = (2 x _____ + (2 x _____)
P = _____ + _____
P = _____

P = 4s
P = 4 x _____
P = _____

2 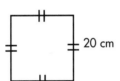 20 cm

3 ft

8 ft

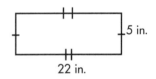 5 in.

22 in.

P = _____

P = _____

P = _____

3 Amber framed a picture using colored string. If the picture is 3 inches tall and 5 inches wide, how much string does she need to go around it once? _____

Name _____

Area of Squares and Rectangles

91

⭐ The **area** is the number of square units needed to cover a figure.

Area of a Square

A = side x side
A = s x s
A = 5 x 5 = 25
The area is 25 sq cm or 25 cm².

Area of a Rectangle

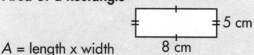
5 cm
8 cm

A = length x width
A = l x w
A = 8 x 5 = 40
The area is 40 sq cm or 40 cm².

Find the area.

1

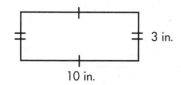
3 in.
10 in.

7 yd

$A = l$ x w
A = _____ x _____
A = _____

$A = s$ x s
A = _____ x _____
A = _____

2

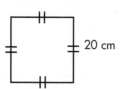
20 cm

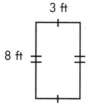
3 ft
8 ft

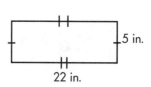
5 in.
22 in.

A = _____

A = _____

A = _____

3 Mrs. Chow covered her living room floor with a new rug. If the room is 12 feet wide and 14 feet long, what is the area of the rug? _____

Area of Parallelograms and Triangles

92

Area of a Parallelogram

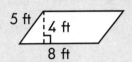

5 ft
4 ft
8 ft

A = base x height
A = b x h
A = 8 x 4 = 32
The area is 32 sq ft or 32 ft².

Area of a Triangle

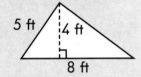

5 ft
4 ft
8 ft

A = ½ x base x height
A = ½ x b x h
A = ½ x 8 x 4 = 16
The area is 16 sq ft or 16 ft².

Find the area.

1

 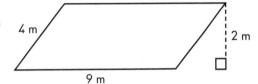

4 m
2 m
9 m

9 in.
15 in.
12 in.

A = b x h
A = _____ x _____
A = _____

A = ½ x b x h
A = ½ x _____ x _____
A = _____

2

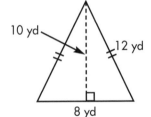

10 yd
12 yd
8 yd

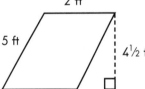

2 ft
5 ft
4½ ft

5 m
7 m

A = _____

A = _____

A = _____

3

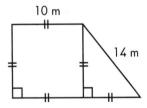

10 m
14 m

4 yd
3 yd
1½ yd   1½ yd

5 cm
10 cm   8 cm
12 cm

A = _____

A = _____

A = _____

Volume of Rectangular Prisms

93

⭐ The **volume** is the number of cubes needed to fill a space or container.

Volume of a Rectangular Prism

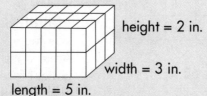

height = 2 in.

width = 3 in.

length = 5 in.

V = length x width x height
$V = l \times w \times h$
$V = 5 \times 3 \times 2 = 30$

The volume is 30 cu in. or 30 inches³.

Find the volume.

1

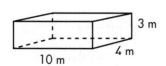

3 m

4 m

10 m

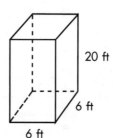

20 ft

6 ft

6 ft

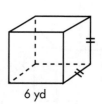

6 yd

$V = l \times w \times h$
$V =$ ____ x ____ x ____
$V =$ _____

$V =$ _____

$V =$ _____

2

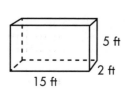

5 ft

2 ft

15 ft

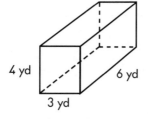

4 yd

6 yd

3 yd

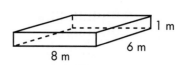

1 m

8 m

6 m

$V =$ _____

$V =$ _____

$V =$ _____

---

3 How many 1-inch cubes are needed to fill a shoe box that is 1 foot long, 6 inches wide, and 4 inches high? _____

Name _____

94

⭐ The **surface area** of a prism is the total area of its faces. It is measured in square units.

Surface Area of a Rectangular Prism

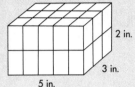

2 in.

3 in.

5 in.

Area of front face   = 5 x 2 = 10
back face   = 5 x 2 = 10
Area of side face   = 3 x 2 = 6
side face   = 3 x 2 = 6
Area of top face   = 5 x 3 = 15
bottom face   = 5 x 3 = 15
Total area of all the faces =   62

The surface area is 62 sq in. or **62 inches².**

Find the surface area.

1

20 ft

6 ft

6 ft

front face   = _____
back face   = _____
side face   = _____
side face   = _____
top face   = _____
bottom face   = _____
Total area   = _____

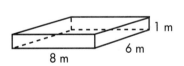

6 yd

_____   _____

2

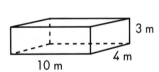

3 m

4 m

10 m

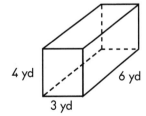

4 yd

6 yd

3 yd

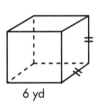

1 m

8 m

6 m

_____   _____   _____

Exact Measurement or an Estimate?

95

⭐ If you only need an estimate to solve the problem, then estimate the answer and tell why. If you need an exact answer to solve the problem, then calculate it and tell why.

Circle one choice.

1 Eric painted a wall 23 feet long and 8 feet high. If a can of paint covers 75 square feet, how many cans of paint did Eric use? _____

EXACT   ESTIMATE

2 A box has a volume of 200 cubic feet. What are the dimensions if the length is twice the width and the height is less than the width? _____

EXACT   ESTIMATE

3 An overpass is 17 feet 4 inches above the highway. Can the driver of a semi truck tell whether his rig will clear the over-pass? _____

EXACT   ESTIMATE

Measurement in Real Life

96

Solve.

1 Miguel began practicing the guitar at 3:15 P.M. He stopped 1 hour 50 minutes later. At what time did Miguel stop practicing? _____

2 The weight of one nickel is about 5 grams. What is the value of a bunch of nickels that has a weight of 1 kilogram? _____

3 Gina framed a painting 34 inches long and 20 inches wide. If the frame material cost $3.95 per foot, how much did it cost Gina to frame the picture? _____

4 How many gallons of juice must Amy buy to have enough 8-ounce glasses of juice for all 27 students in her class on a picnic? _____

5 How much carpet would cover the floor of a room 21 feet long and 12 feet wide? If the carpeting cost $20 per square yard, what was the cost? _____

6 Abdul has a fish tank 80 cm long, 40 cm wide, and 25 cm high. He filled the tank with water so that it's 3 cm from the top. How many liters of water did he use? (1 liter of water = 1,000 cu cm) _____

Name _____

1
8 ft 10 in.
+ 6 ft 8 in.
_____

○ 14 ft 2 in.   ○ $14\frac{1}{2}$ ft

○ $15\frac{1}{2}$ ft   ○ $3\frac{1}{2}$ yd

2 A house door is about 2 _____ high.
○ mm
○ cm
○ m
○ km

3 112 oz = _____ lbs
○ 7
○ 9.3
○ 14
○ 784

4 6½ gal = _____ qt
○ 13
○ 26
○ 39
○ 52

5 A glass of water is about 250 _____.
○ fl oz
○ mg
○ L
○ mL

6 The temperature warm enough to go swimming is about _____.
○ 30°C
○ 30°F
○ 60°F
○ 90°C

7 Start: 9:30 A.M.
Stop: 2:20 P.M.
How much time elapsed?
○ 7 h 10 min
○ 5 h 10 min
○ 4 h 50 min
○ 5 h 10 min

8 Kirk went to lunch at 11:45 A.M. He ate lunch for 1 hour and 20 minutes. When did he finish lunch?
○ 10:25 A.M.
○ 12:05 P.M.
○ 12:55 P.M.
○ 1:05 P.M.

Name _____

98

Fill in the bubble beside the correct answer.

---

1 The perimeter is _____.
- ○ 25 m
- ○ 18 m
- ○ 50 m
- ○ 50 sq m

15 m
10 m

---

2 The area is _____.
- ○ 19 ft
- ○ 38 ft
- ○ 10 sq ft
- ○ 48 sq ft

3 ft
16 ft

---

3 The perimeter is _____.
- ○ 20 in.
- ○ 40 in.
- ○ 60 in.
- ○ 80 in.

20 in.

---

4 The area is _____.
- ○ 30 m
- ○ 30 sq m
- ○ 36 sq m
- ○ 65 sq m

13 m
6 m
12 m

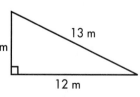

---

5 An Asian elephant is 132 inches tall. If a man is 2 yards tall, how much taller is the elephant?
- ○ 130 in.
- ○ 100 in.
- ○ 5 ft
- ○ 1⅓ ft

---

6 How much money is saved buying one gallon of juice for $4.79 instead of 4 quarts of the same juice for $1.29 a quart?
- ○ $0.37
- ○ $1.37
- ○ $2.21
- ○ $3.50

---

7 The volume is _____.
- ○ 12 ft
- ○ 12 sq ft
- ○ 24 cu ft
- ○ 36 cu ft

3 ft
2 ft
6 ft

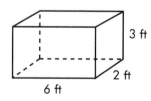

---

8 The surface area is _____.
- ○ 24 cu ft
- ○ 36 cu ft
- ○ 72 sq ft
- ○ 216 sq ft

3 ft
2 ft
6 ft

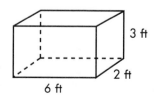

Practice Test

99

Fill in the bubble beside the correct answer.

1 7,046 − 2,789 =
- ○ 4,257
- ○ 4,343
- ○ 5,743
- ○ 9,835

2 509 × 78 =
- ○ 587
- ○ 4,072
- ○ 4,602
- ○ 39,702

3 3,700 ÷ 48 =
- ○ 7 R34
- ○ 75
- ○ 77 R4
- ○ 79 R8

4 The value of 6 in 25.368 is _____.
- ○ 6 tens
- ○ 6 tenths
- ○ 6 hundredths
- ○ 6 thousandths

5 1.3 × 0.09 =
- ○ 117
- ○ 1.17
- ○ 0.117
- ○ 0.0017

6 The number _____ is neither prime nor composite.
- ○ 3
- ○ 2
- ○ 1
- ○ 0

7 Which number is greater than 0.7?
- ○ 8%
- ○ $^3/_{25}$
- ○ 0.09
- ○ $^4/_5$

8 $\dfrac{7}{8} + \dfrac{2}{3} =$
- ○ $\dfrac{9}{11}$
- ○ $\dfrac{9}{24}$
- ○ $1\dfrac{1}{2}$
- ○ $1\dfrac{13}{24}$

Name _____

Practice Test

100

Fill in the bubble beside the correct answer.

---

1 $9\frac{1}{8} - 3\frac{3}{4} =$

○ $6\frac{5}{8}$ ○ $6\frac{1}{4}$

○ $5\frac{5}{8}$ ○ $5\frac{3}{8}$

---

2 $1\frac{7}{8} \times \frac{4}{5} =$

○ $1\frac{1}{2}$ ○ $1\frac{3}{40}$

○ $2\frac{37}{40}$ ○ $2\frac{7}{10}$

---

3 P(odd number) = _____

○ ⅙
○ ⅓
○ ⅔
○ ½

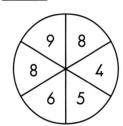

---

4 What is the median for this data?

○ 15
○ 40
○ 42
○ 45

| 40, 45, 50, 35, 40 |

---

5 How many students are in grade 4?

○ 45
○ 50
○ 55
○ 95

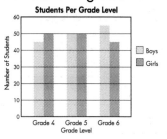

---

6 This triangle is ____ and ____.

○ right, isosceles
○ acute, isosceles
○ obtuse, scalene
○ obtuse, isosceles

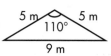

---

7 These lines are _____.

○ perpendicular
○ parallel
○ scalene
○ right

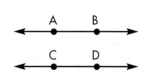

---

8 The area is _____.

○ 19 m²
○ 36 m²
○ 45 m²
○ 180 m²

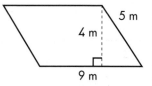

Name _____

Math Grade 5 Tracking Sheet

Activity	Possible	My Score
Unit 1		
1	14	
2	17	
3	16	
4	26	
5	16	
6	20	
7	14	
8	18	
9	16	
10	18	
11	22	
12	6	
Test Scores		
13	8	
14	8	
Unit 2		
15	18	
16	15	
17	14	
18	26	
19	21	
20	32	
21	14	
22	26	
23	14	
24	18	
Test Scores		
25	8	

Activity	Possible	My Score
26	8	
Unit 3		
27	8	
28	7	
29	16	
30	21	
31	15	
32	9	
33	9	
34	19	
Test Scores		
35	8	
36	8	
Unit 4		
37	9	
38	24	
39	21	
40	15	
41	21	
42	16	
43	15	
44	17	
45	11	
46	11	
47	18	
48	11	
49	17	
50	16	
51	18	

Activity	Possible	My Score
52	18	
Test Scores		
53	8	
54	8	
Unit 5		
55	9	
56	18	
57	15	
58	13	
59	6	
60	6	
61	8	
62	9	
63	4	
64	5	
65	7	
66	5	
67	5	
68	5	
69	6	
70	10	
Test Scores		
71	8	
72	8	
Unit 6		
73	10	
74	15	
75	8	
76	7	

Activity	Possible	My Score
77	16	
78	12	
79	5	
80	8	
Test Scores		
81	8	
82	7	
Unit 7		
83	14	
84	16	
85	23	
86	18	
87	12	
88	13	
89	10	
90	6	
91	6	
92	8	
93	7	
94	5	
95	3	
96	6	
Test Scores		
97	8	
98	8	
99	8	
100	8	

Math 5 Answer Key

Activity 1
1. 65,409
2. 26,503,070
3. 380,000,045
4. 70,070,070
5. 932,408,000
6. 400,300,700
7. 3 hundred   3 thousand
8. 3 thousand   30 million
9. 30 thousand   30
10. 93,000,000
11. 141 million, 710 thousand

Activity 2
1. >   <
2. <   <
3. <   >
4. <   >
5. >   >
6. 348, 438 , 834, 843
7. 45,672; 45,692; 46,762
8. 325,750; 325,805; 327,605
9. 1,373,917; 1,375,617; 1,375,671
10. 63,367; 63,736; 67,376; 67,673
11. Lincoln School
12. Franklin School

Activity 3
Estimations may vary.
1. 5,000 + 800 = 5,800
2. 4,000 − 2,000 = 2,000
3. 1,000 − 700 = 300
4. 20,000 + 7,000 = 27,000
5. 400,000 − 100,000 = 300,000
6. 400,000 + 50,000 = 450,000
7. 3,600   6,000
8. 14,000   50,000
9. 32,000   12,000
10. 100,000   1,100,000
11. about 2,000 pieces of fruit
12. about 8,000 people

Activity 4
1. 142   27   1,022
   67   390   381
2. 1,171   2,397   90,000
   20,633   6,435   5,782
3. 125   5,679   9,793

21,276   635,313   575,757
4. 4,288   122,589   312,971
   642,766 123,845   411,809
5. 48,739 people
6. 3,783 students

Activity 5
1. 6 x 800 = 4,800
2. 5000 x 10 = 50,000
3. 400 x 50 = 20,000
4. 600 x 100 = 60,000
5. 700 x 40 = 28,000
6. 600 x 70 = 42,000
7. 1,000   24,000
8. 21,000   300,000
9. 210,000   12,000,000
10. 28,000,000   240,000
11. 200,000 widgets
12. 80,000 widgets

Activity 6
1. 2,556   960   19,722
   23,414   586,683 113,463
2. 3,128   25,079   23,940
   31,948   10,045   10,815
3. 289,256   208,740 90,513
   226,803   429,374 218,944
4. 27,936 crackers
5. 70,320 pairs

Activity 7
1. 400 ÷ 80 = 5
   400 ÷ 50 = 8
2. 5,000 ÷ 40 = 125
   800 ÷ 80 = 10
3. 2,000 ÷ 80 = 25
   8,000 ÷ 20 = 400
4. 10   20
5. 100   50
6. 80   10
7. 3 books
8. 100 people

Activity 8
1. 24   19   34   4
2. 7   8   30   30
3. 56   78 R20
   67   45 R4
4. 379 R13 105 R20
   104 R3   718 R2

5. 18 classes
6. 42 buses

Activity 9
1. $n - 9$
2. $n/3$ or $(n \div 3)$
3. $n + 6$
4. $6n$
5. $n - 4$
6. $2n$
7. 20   3   36
8. 8   4   12
9. 48   6
10. 8   20

Activity 10
1. 12   12   61
2. 46   0   24
3. 1   5   22
4. 60   30   80
5. 18   6   3
6. 54   5   90

Activity 11
1. 3,937   28,497   9,300
   32 R16
2. 58,887   91,370   142
   17,433
3. 31,142   50,547   43,122
   809 R1
4. 17,090   32,338   520 R40
   34,427
5. $a = 46$ $t = 5$ $d = 66$
   $n = 36$
6. 30 blueberries
7. 28 blueberries with 136 blueberries left over

Activity 12
1. 360 CDs
2. 152 points
3. 127 students
4. 26 miles
5. 1,305   1,254
   1,095   987
6. 4,641 points

Activity 13—Take a Test Drive
1. 2,065,090
2. 3,000

3. 46,770
4. 83,033   83,303   83,330
5. 2,500
6. 35,000
7. 6,000 – 3,000
8. 24 ÷ 4

Activity 14—Take a Test Drive
1. 2,527
2. 32,637
3. 82,800
4. 75
5. multiplication
6. 24
7. 32
8. 82

Activity 15
1. 0.42   4.008
2. 0.567   10.1
3. 700   0.07
4. tenths   hundredths
5. ones   thousandths
6. tens   hundredths
7. 0.07, $^7/_{100}$ 0.7, $^7/_{10}$
8. 0.07, $^7/_{100}$ 7.0, $^7/_1$
9. 0.007, $^7/_{1,000}$ 0.007, $^7/_{1,000}$

Activity 16
1. <   <
2. >   <
3. >   >
4. >   >
5. 4.007   4.07   4.7
6. 0.64   6.04   6.4
7. 0.009   0.09   0.90
8. 7.053   7.503   75.03
9. 2.016   2.36   2.6
10. 0.75 ounce
11. between 2:00 and 3:00

Activity 17
1. 7 + 3 = 10
   8 – 2 = 6
   3 – 1 = 2
2. $6 + $2 = $8
   $10 – $8 = $2
   3 – 0 = 3
3. 6 $3
4. 4   7
5. $2   7
6. $14
7. $14

Activity 18
1. 7.96   5.04   6.16
   6.431 $5.76 $11.57
2. 0.736   5.64   9.07
   4.63   2.119   3.528
3. 3.581   5.79   0.383
   8.939   6.378   8.03
4. 5.622 $1.25   0.51
   0.32   13.76 $1.50
5. $3.65
6. 1.8 inches

Activity 19
1. 32.6   4.6
   326   46
   3,260   460
2. by 10:   38   6.2   1.4
   by 100:   420   76   3.5
   by 1,000:   1,500   32   750
3. 25   4.7   1,700
4. 70   80.6   8.3
5. 1,590   383   60.08
6. 832   4,160   50

Activity 20
1. 270.5   3.517   27.05
2. 0.3517   2.705   0.03517
3. 0.237   7.58   4.3
4. 4.256   3.86   7.451
5. 0.632   0.0058   0.0308
6. 0.086   3.262   0.075
7. 3.7   7.58   .00046
8. 8.351   0.038   4.305
9. 0.00009   7.506   0.00105
10. 0.3056   0.0362   1.002
11. $4.50
12. $45.00

Activity 21
1. 4 x 8 = 32 $9 x 4 = $36
2. 5 x 6 = 30   8 x $6 = $48
3. 1 x 3 = 3   7 x 3 = 21
4. 28 $7
5. 21 $15
6. 30   50
7. Chloe cannot buy all the fabric.
   She needs about $108 (or
   exactly $107.10).
8. Yes, when estimating it may not
   look like it, but the boards will
   cost exactly $71.50.

Activity 22
1. 10.73   19.468   0.56

2.336   2.35   0.63
2. $52.21 (exactly $52.207)
   2.418 $19.24   114.81
   0.048   1,722.82
3. 17.02 $143.70   0.085
   $28   0.0024   1.3635
4. 28.5   4.29   7.2
   $15   90 $29.91
5. $17.50
6. $1.75

Activity 23
1. 1.37 $1.42   0.631
   2.08 $0.42   0.15
2. 0.015   0.016   9.66
   $3.42   4.06   2.79
3. $5.25
4. $1.50

Activity 24
1. 10.39   4.52   3.75   5.006
2. $6.46   31.218   5.24   0.065
3. 2.15   1.13 $95.85   2.09
4. 2,690   4.836
5. 0.57   5.07   7.05   7.5
6. 0.395   3.95   39.5   395
7. 0.017   0.17   1.70   170
8. 0.4   0.45   0.451   0.532

Activity 25—Take a Test Drive
1. 0.35
2. tenths
3. 6 hundredths
4. 2.60
5. <
6. 4.009   4.09   4.9
7. 2 places to the right
8. 35.82

Activity 26—Take a Test Drive
1. 8
2. 5
3. 8.87
4. 1.43
5. 14.652
6. 0.072
7. 2.74
8. 0.32

Activity 27
5. 25
6. 2   97
7. 2, 3, 5, 7, 11, 13, 17, 19, 23, 29
8. 31, 37, 41, 43, 47, 53, 59, 61,

67, 71, 73, 79, 83, 89, 97

Activity 28
1. 1, 23   prime
2. 1, 2, 4, 8, 16, 32   composite
3. 1, 37   prime
4. 3 x 2 x 2   3 x 3 x 2
5. 5 x 2 x 2 x 2   3 x 3 x 3

Activity 29
1. 2, 5, 10   3
2. 2, 3, 6   2
3. 2   2, 5, 10
4. 2   2, 3, 5, 6, 10
5. 1, 3, 7, 21
     1, 2, 3, 5, 6, 10, 15, 30
6. 1, 2, 4, 7, 8, 14, 28, 56
     1, 2, 3, 6, 7, 14, 21, 42
7. 1, 2, 4, 8, 16, 32, 64
     1, 2, 4, 5, 8, 10, 16, 20, 40, 80
8. 1, 2, 3, 4, 6, 8, 12, 16, 24, 32, 48, 96
     1, 2, 4, 5, 10, 20, 25, 50, 100

Activity 30
1. 18: 1, 2, 3, 6, 9, 18
     8: 1, 2, 4, 8
     circle 2
     24: 1, 2, 3, 4, 6, 8, 12, 24
     20: 1, 2, 4, 5, 10, 20
     circle 4
2. 10: 1, 2, 5, 10
     15: 1, 3, 5, 15
     circle 5
     25: 1, 5, 25
     24: 1, 2, 3, 4, 6, 8, 12, 24
     circle 1
3. 24: 1, 2, 3, 4, 6, 8, 12, 24
     36: 1, 2, 3, 4, 6, 9, 12, 18, 36
     circle 12
     40: 1, 2, 4, 5, 8, 10, 20, 40
     16: 1, 2, 4, 8, 16
     circle 8
4. 5   6   1   12   5
5. 6   1   3   7   8
6. 3   6   3   5   8

Activity 31
1. 4: 4, 8, 12, 16, 20, 24, 28, 32, 36, 40
     5: 5, 10, 15, 20, 25, 30, 35, 40, 45, 50
     circle 20
     6: 6, 12, 18, 24, 30, 36, 42,

48, 54, 60
     3: 3, 6, 9, 12, 15, 18, 21, 24, 27, 30
     circle 6
2. 2: 2, 4, 6, 8, 10, 12, 14, 16, 18, 20
     9: 9, 18, 27, 36, 45, 54, 63, 72, 81, 90
     circle 18
     7: 7, 14, 21, 28, 35, 42, 49, 56, 63, 70
     4: 4, 8, 12, 16, 20, 24, 28, 32, 36, 40
     circle 28
3. 8: 8, 16, 24, 32, 40, 48, 56, 64, 72, 80
     6: 6, 12, 18, 24, 30, 36, 42, 48, 54, 60
     circle 24
     10: 10, 20, 30, 40, 50, 60, 70, 80, 90, 100
     8: 8, 16, 24, 32, 40, 48, 56, 64, 72, 80
     circle 40
4. 15   18   24
5. 30   42   25
6. 36   12   90

Activity 32
1. 4: 4, 8, 12, 16
     6: 6, 12
     LCD: 12
2. 8: 8, 16, 24
     12: 12, 24
     LCD: 24
3. 3: 3, 6, 9, 12, 15
     5: 5, 10, 15
     LCD: 15
4. 15   12   18
5. 36   20   50

Activity 33
1. 36, 30, 24   – 6
2. 96, 192, 384   x 2
3. 512, 2,048, 8,192   x 4
4. 11, 16, 13   + 5, – 3
5. 10.2, 11.3, 12.4   +1.1
6. 74, 76, 66   – 10, + 2
7. 2¼, 2¾, 3¼   + ½
8. ¹⁄₃₂, ¹⁄₆₄, ¹⁄₁₂₈   ÷ 2 (or x ½)
9. 45, 36, 27   – 9

Activity 34
1. Add 6:

Input: 49   Output: 29   46
Divide by 3:
Input: 24   Output: 15   20
Subtract 5:
Input: 40   Output: 45   0
2. +4   x5   –7
3. 1   4   9   16   25   36
4. 49   64   81   100   121   144
5. Add increasing odd numbers, +3, +5, +7, +9, …

Activity 35—Take a Test Drive
1. 43
2. 33
3. 1, 2, 3, 4, 6, 9, 12, 18, 36
4. 5
5. prime
6. 1
7. 6 and 9
8. 6

Activity 36—Take a Test Drive
1. 3
2. 40
3. 24
4. 64, 128, 256
5. add 4, subtract 1
6. 0
7. 12
8. subtract 7

Activity 37
1. ⅝   ¼   ⅚
2. ½   ⁴⁰⁄₁₀₀   ⅔
3. ⁹⁄₁₀₀, 0.09   ⁷⁄₁₀, 0.7   ³⁄₁₀, 0.3

Activity 38
1. 4   10   10   3   2   4
2. 30   6   9   2   9   42
3. 21   18   16   35   33   16
4. ⁴⁄₁₆, ⁵⁄₂₀, ⁶⁄₂₄   ⁸⁄₂₀, ¹⁰⁄₂₅, ¹²⁄₃₀
5. ⁸⁄₁₂, ¹⁰⁄₁₅, ¹²⁄₁₈   ⅖
6. ⁴⁄₂₈, ⁵⁄₃₅, ⁶⁄₄₂   ⁴⁄₂₄, ⁵⁄₃₀, ⁶⁄₃₆

Activity 39
1. ⅗   ⅔   ⅓   4⁄₇   ¼
2. ¾   ⅝   ⅔   ⅚   ¾
3. ¾   ⁹⁄₁₄   ½   ¹⁵⁄₁₆   ⁵⁄₉
4. ⅓   ⅔   ⅖   ⅙   ¹⁄₅₀
5. ⁴⁄₁₀

Activity 40
1. <   >   =
2. >   =   >

3. > < >
4. $\frac{3}{8}, \frac{1}{2}, \frac{3}{4}$ $\frac{1}{2}, \frac{3}{5}, \frac{7}{10}$
5. $\frac{1}{2}, \frac{2}{3}, \frac{3}{4}$ $\frac{3}{5}, \frac{7}{10}, \frac{3}{4}$
6. Dylan ate more.
7. Wiggly Worm is longer.

Activity 41
1. $2\frac{1}{2}$ $2\frac{1}{2}$ $1\frac{1}{3}$
$1\frac{1}{3}$ $4\frac{1}{2}$
2. $4\frac{1}{2}$ 6 $1\frac{2}{5}$
$2\frac{2}{5}$ $8\frac{1}{3}$
3. $\frac{13}{3}$ $\frac{13}{8}$ $\frac{18}{5}$
$\frac{17}{3}$ $\frac{71}{7}$
4. $\frac{17}{2}$ $\frac{29}{10}$ $\frac{19}{3}$
$\frac{21}{5}$ $\frac{709}{100}$
5. 5 sandwiches

Activity 42
1. < = >
2. < > =
3. $\frac{5}{8}$, 0.65, $\frac{2}{3}$, 0.7
0.070, $\frac{9}{5}$, 1.64, $1\frac{7}{8}$
4. C A D B
5. D C A B

Activity 43
1. $\frac{1}{2}$ 1 0 $\frac{1}{2}$ 1
2. circle: $\frac{11}{12} + \frac{7}{9}$
$\frac{1}{6} + \frac{11}{12}$
$\frac{5}{12} + \frac{5}{8}$
3. $\frac{1}{2} + 1 = 1\frac{1}{2}$
$1 - \frac{1}{4} = \frac{3}{4}$
$0 + \frac{1}{2} = \frac{1}{2}$
4. 1 $\frac{1}{2}$ $\frac{1}{2}$
5. 1 2 $\frac{1}{2}$

Activity 44
1. $\frac{2}{3}$ $\frac{3}{8}$ 1
2. $1\frac{2}{5}$ $\frac{9}{15} = \frac{3}{5}$ $1\frac{1}{3}$
3. $\frac{2}{5}$ $1\frac{1}{2}$ $\frac{1}{2}$
4. $1\frac{1}{4}$ $\frac{2}{3}$ $\frac{1}{6}$
5. $6\frac{1}{5}$ $2\frac{1}{4}$ $6\frac{1}{3}$
6. $2\frac{1}{2}$ inches
7. $\frac{1}{2}$ tank

Activity 45
1. $1\frac{1}{2}$ $1\frac{3}{20}$ $1\frac{1}{2}$
2. $\frac{2}{3}$ $\frac{5}{6}$ $\frac{11}{12}$
3. $1\frac{5}{24}$ $1\frac{5}{12}$ $1\frac{23}{40}$
4. $1\frac{1}{12}$
5. $\frac{9}{20}$ can

Activity 46
1. $\frac{1}{3}$ $\frac{1}{2}$ $\frac{1}{3}$
2. $\frac{7}{12}$ $\frac{4}{15}$ $\frac{1}{2}$
3. $\frac{3}{20}$ $\frac{1}{24}$ $\frac{13}{24}$
4. $\frac{5}{12}$ foot
5. $\frac{5}{12}$ of his rabbits

Activity 47
1. 2 5 4 1 7
2. $6 - 2 = 4$
$4 + 5 = 9$
$4 - 1 = 3$
3. 1 9 9
4. 0 9 10
5. 7 6
6. 10 6

Activity 48
1. $12\frac{1}{8}$ $8\frac{8}{9}$ $4\frac{1}{8}$
2. $11\frac{3}{10}$ $4\frac{1}{12}$ $10\frac{5}{12}$
3. $11\frac{1}{12}$ $5\frac{11}{12}$ $8\frac{5}{9}$
4. $12\frac{11}{40}$
5. $3\frac{11}{12}$ cups

Activity 49
1. 5 9 8 13 108
2. $2\frac{7}{10}$ $2\frac{1}{2}$ $1\frac{3}{8}$
3. $4\frac{5}{8}$ $1\frac{3}{8}$ $\frac{9}{10}$
4. $3\frac{1}{12}$ $6\frac{1}{6}$ $4\frac{23}{24}$
5. $1\frac{1}{2}$ $1\frac{5}{8}$ $1\frac{5}{6}$

Activity 50
1. $1\frac{1}{2}$ $\frac{4}{9}$ 15
2. $\frac{19}{24}$ $\frac{7}{18}$ $4\frac{1}{6}$
3. $1\frac{5}{12}$ $\frac{3}{10}$ $\frac{1}{12}$
4. $6\frac{1}{8}$ $\frac{19}{40}$ $1\frac{1}{2}$
5. $3\frac{1}{4}$ $1\frac{1}{2}$ $8\frac{7}{24}$
6. $\frac{7}{12}$ cup

Activity 51
1. $\frac{1}{9}$ $\frac{1}{4}$ $\frac{9}{2} = 4\frac{1}{2}$
2. $\frac{3}{10}$ $\frac{1}{3}$ $\frac{5}{48}$
3. $\frac{2}{5}$ $\frac{3}{8}$ 6
4. $\frac{1}{3}$ $\frac{5}{3} = 1\frac{2}{3}$ $\frac{1}{9}$
5. $\frac{5}{18}$ $\frac{3}{20}$ 3
6. $\frac{4}{3} = 1\frac{1}{3}$ $\frac{9}{14}$ $\frac{1}{2}$

Activity 52
1. $\frac{3}{2} = 1\frac{1}{2}$
$\frac{5}{2} = 2\frac{1}{2}$ 1
2. 20
$\frac{25}{12} = 2\frac{1}{12}$
$\frac{22}{3} = 7\frac{1}{3}$
3. $\frac{20}{3} = 6\frac{2}{3}$
$\frac{15}{4} = 3\frac{3}{4}$
$\frac{14}{3} = 4\frac{2}{3}$
4. $\frac{28}{3} = 9\frac{1}{3}$
$\frac{49}{4} = 12\frac{1}{4}$
$\frac{33}{2} = 16\frac{1}{2}$
5. $\frac{21}{4} = 5\frac{1}{4}$
$\frac{92}{5} = 14\frac{2}{5}$
$\frac{55}{6} = 9\frac{1}{6}$
6. 15
$\frac{99}{16} = 6\frac{3}{16}$
$\frac{55}{3} = 18\frac{1}{3}$

Activity 53—Take a Test Drive
1. $\frac{9}{12}$
2. $\frac{7}{10}$
3. $\frac{9}{12}$
4. $\frac{3}{4}$
5. $\frac{4}{3}$
6. $\frac{1}{2}$
7. $2\frac{4}{5}$
8. $2\frac{1}{2}$

Activity 54—Take a Test Drive
1. $\frac{5}{8}, \frac{2}{3}$, 0.7
2. $\frac{5}{6} < 1.5$
3. $1\frac{1}{2}$
4. $\frac{5}{6}$
5. $\frac{19}{36}$
6. $5\frac{1}{12}$
7. $1\frac{1}{2}$
8. 3

Activity 55
1. $\frac{10}{100}$, 0.10, 10%
$\frac{36}{100}$, 0.36, 36%
$\frac{8}{100}$, 0.08, 8%
2. $\frac{50}{100}$, 0.5, 50%
$\frac{100}{100}$, 1, 100%
$\frac{25}{100}$, 0.25, 25%
3. $\frac{20}{100}$, 0.2, 20%
$\frac{82}{100}$, 0.82, 82%
$\frac{1}{100}$, 0.01, 1%

Activity 56
1. $\frac{1}{5}$ $\frac{1}{4}$ $\frac{1}{10}$ $\frac{3}{4}$
2. $\frac{3}{10}$ $\frac{1}{2}$ $\frac{1}{50}$ $\frac{9}{25}$
3. 25% 60% 35% 90%
4. 75% 24% 9% 100%
5. $\frac{2}{5}$, 0.4, 40% $\frac{2}{25}$, 0.08, 8%
$\frac{7}{20}$, 0.35, 35% $\frac{3}{25}$, 0.12, 12%
$\frac{3}{20}$, 0.15, 15% $\frac{4}{25}$, 0.16, 16%

Activity 57
1. = > >
2. < > =
3. < < <

4. <   >   <
5. 7%, 7/20, 0.70
6. 36%, 9/20, 3.6
7. 0.09, 9/10, 99%

Activity 58
1. 39   24   2
2. 24   90   64
3. 9   140   80
4. 2 shots
5. 12 baskets
6. 7 students
7. 12 students

Activity 59
1. 1, 2, 3, 4, 5, 6
   equally
   A, B, C, D, E, F, G, H
   equally
2. dots, stripes, solid, squiggly lines
   equally
   blue, red, green
   less
3. 5, 6, 7, 8
   equally
   triangle, circle, rectangle, hexagon
   more

Activity 60
1. 1/6, 1/2, 1/2   1/5, 2/5, 4/5
2. 1/4, 1/4, 0/8   1/6, 1/2, 5/6
3. 2/5 probability
4. 0/5 (impossible)

Activity 61
1. R: 5, Mo: 12, Med: 12
   R: 15, Mo: 40, Med: 40
2. R: 32, Mo: none, Med: 66
   R: 15, Mo: 100, Med: 95
3. R: 29, Mo: none, Med: 119
   R: 3, Mo: 20, 21 Med: 21
4. none
5. 74

Activity 62
1. 21   12   68.5
2. 68.9   92.5
3. 90
4. 40 and 20
5. 86
6. 1 point

Activity 63
1. R: 4, Mo: 7, Med: 7, Mean: 7

R: 8, Mo: 92, Med: 95, Mean: 95
2. R: 7, Mo: 2 and 7, Med: 6,
   Mean: 5
   R: 8, Mo: 61, Med: 58, Mean: 59

Activity 64
1. R: 18, Mo: 77, Med: 76, Mean: 74
   R: 19, Mo: 88, 92, and 95,
   Med: 92, Mean: 90 (89.888)
2.

Stems	Leaves
2	5 6 8
3	1 3 5 7
4	3 6

   R: 21, Mo: none, Med: 33,
   Mean: 34 (33.777)
3.

Stems	Leaves
4	2 3 6
5	5 5
6	1 1 2 3

   R: 21, Mo: 55 and 61, Med: 55,
   Mean: 54 (54.222)
4.

Stems	Leaves
1	5 5 7 7
2	2 4 6
3	1 1

   R: 16, Mo: 15, 17, and 31,
   Med: 22, Mean: 22

Activity 65
1. 50 mph
2. 25 mph
3. cheetah
4. lion
5. rabbit
6. elephant
7. 40 mph

Activity 66
1. 16 boys
2. 6 girls
3. 26 boys and girls
4. 4 more
5. dogs

Activity 67
1. 28 students
2. 22 students
3. 4 more
4. Tuesday and Wednesday
5. Friday

Activity 68
1. 30 sandwiches
2. 20 sandwiches

3. 12 noon
4. between 10 A.M. and 12 noon
5. 20 sandwiches

Activity 69
1. 100 students
2. 400 students
3. 1/4
4. 50%
5. 1/10
6. 75%

Activity 70
1. line plot
2. double line graph
3. double bar graph
4. circle graph
5. stem-and-leaf graph
6. line graph
7. circle graph
8. double bar graph
9. stem-and-leaf graph
10. double line graph

Activity 71—Take a Test Drive
1. 35%
2. 2/5
3. 45%
4. 0.08
5. 4/5
6. 9%, 9/20, 0.9
7. 12
8. 1/2

Activity 72—Take a Test Drive
1. median
2. 7
3. 52
4. 53
5. 45
6. 25
7. 50%
8. line graph

Activity 73
1.

2.

Sample answers given:
3. $\overrightarrow{AB}$, $\overrightarrow{AC}$, $\overrightarrow{CD}$, $\overrightarrow{BD}$

4. $\overrightarrow{AC}$
5. $\overleftrightarrow{AB}$, $\overleftrightarrow{CD}$
6. $\overleftrightarrow{AC}$, $\overleftrightarrow{CD}$

Activity 74
cube, square, 8
pyramid, triangle or square, 7
rectangular prism, rectangle, equal

Quadrilateral	Pairs of Parallel Lines	Has Right Angles	Has Equal Sides
Parallelogram	yes	no	no
Rhombus	yes	no	yes
Rectangle	yes	yes	no
Square	yes	yes	yes

Activity 75
1. acute, less than
   obtuse, greater than
   right, equal to
Sample answers given:
2. ∠JBA, ∠KCB
3. ∠ABF, ∠KCD
4. ∠BFG, ∠CGH
5. ∠ACD, ∠KCG
6. acute angle

Activity 76
1. right, isosceles acute, equilateral
   obtuse, scalene
2. 48°   both are 70°
   all are 60°   105°

Activity 77
1. A (5,3), B (10,7), C (0,0), D (1,6),
   E (6,0), F (0,8), G (6,10), H (3,4)
2.
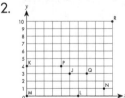

Activity 78
1. flip   slide   turn
2. turn   flip   slide
3.

4.

Activity 79
1. similar   congruent
2. neither   similar
3. Circles are always similar
   because they are always the
   same shape; although they are
   often a different size.

Activity 80
1. P
2. $\overline{QS}$, $\overline{WR}$
Sample answers given:
3. $\overline{VT}$
4. $\overline{WP}$, $\overline{PS}$, $\overline{QP}$
5–8.

Activity 81—Take a Test Drive
1. perpendicular
2. ray
3. cube, square
4. rectangular prism
5. obtuse
6. acute
7. right, scalene
8. equilateral, right

Activity 82—Take a Test Drive
1. (3,6)
2. E
3. slide
4. the first shape on the left
5. similar
6. the last shape on the right
7. $\overline{AB}$ (sample answer)

Activity 83
1. 60 in.
   5 yd
   8 ft
2. 15,840 ft
   53 in.
   5 ft 10 in.
3. 3⅓ ft
   1,760 yd
   1⅓ yd
4. 9 yd
   2 yd 2 ft
   2 mi 2,580 ft
   13 yd 8 in.
5. 1 ft 7 in. taller

Activity 84
1. 350	1.5	2,300
2. 2.05	37	310
3. 0.65	0.35	5,000
4. m		
5. cm		
6. km		
7. m		
8. mm		
9. cm	cm	
10. cm		

Activity 85
1. 3	12,000	6
2. 5,000	¾	1¾
3. 12	12	12
4. 24	2½	14
5. 2½	24	32
6. 1½	1	3
7. 2	1,000	1
8. Megan's cat
9. Luis

Activity 86
1. 8,000	5,000	4.8
2. 0.75	300	6,500
3. 2,000	6.9	3,500
4. 0.37	90	0.005
5. mL
6. L
7. kg
8. g
9. mg
10. mg

Activity 87
1. milk 38°F   water 90°F
   fever 103°F   rink 15°F
2. juice 10°C   water 30°C
   ice 0°C   room 20°C
Sample answers given:
3. stay inside, warm clothes
4. go sledding, winter coats
5. build a snowman, winter coat
6. go swimming, shorts

Activity 88
1. 5 h 10 min   2 yr 40 wk
   3 min 35 sec   10 h
2. 4 h 45 min   6 h 45 min
   7 h 15 min   8 h 30 min
3. 3:20 P.M.   11:15 A.M.
   5:15 P.M.   11:05 P.M.
4. 35 min

Activity 89
1. 22 m   33 in.   8 m
2. 40 ft   28 m   32 yd
3. 24 in.   15 yd   24 m
    16 ft

Activity 90
1. $(2 \times 10) + (2 \times 3)$
   $20 + 6 = 26$ in.
   $4 \times 7 = 28$ yd
2. 80 cm   22 ft   54 in.
3. 16 in.

Activity 91
1. $10 \times 3 = 30$ sq in.
   $7 \times 7 = 49$ sq yd
2. 400 sq cm
   24 sq ft
   110 sq in.
3. 168 sq ft

Activity 92
1. $9 \times 2 = 18$ sq m
   $\frac{1}{2} \times 12 \times 9 = 54$ sq in.
2. 40 sq yd
   9 sq ft
   35 sq m
3. 170 sq m
   16.5 sq yd
   88 sq cm

Activity 93
1. $10 \times 4 \times 3 = 120$ cu m
   720 cu ft
   216 cu yd
2. 150 cu ft
   72 cu yd
   48 cu m
3. 288 cubes

Activity 94
1. ff = 120 sq ft, bf = 120 sq ft,
   sf = 120 sq ft, sf = 120 sq ft,
   tf = 36 sq ft, bf = 36 sq ft,
   Total area = 552 sq ft
   216 sq yd
2. 164 sq m
   108 sq yd
   124 sq m

Activity 95
1. Estimate—he probably won't
   use an exact number of cans,
   so over-estimate: 23 ft x 8 ft

is about $25 \times 8 = 200$ sq ft,
divide 200 by 75 to get a
number over 2, so Eric will
use 3 cans of paint.
2. Exact—it is asking for exact
   measurements. Sample answer
   given: length = 20 ft,
   width = 10 ft, height = 1 ft.
3. Estimate—but overestimate to
   be sure; use exact if it is close.

Activity 96
1. 5:05 P.M.
2. $1000 \div 5 = 200 \times \$0.05 = \$10$
3. 108 in = 9 ft $\times \$3.95 = \$35.55$
4. $216 \div 128 = 1.68$ gal =
   2 gallons
5. 252 sq ft $\div 3 = 84 \times \$20 =$
   \$1,680
6. 80 cm x 40 cm x 22 cm =
   70,400 cu cm = 70.4 L

Activity 97—Practice Test
1. $15\frac{1}{2}$ ft
2. m
3. 7
4. 26
5. mL
6. 30°C
7. 4 h 50 min
8. 1:05 P.M.

Activity 98—Practice Test
1. 50 m
2. 48 sq ft
3. 80 in.
4. 36 sq m
5. 5 ft
6. \$0.37
7. 36 cu ft
8. 72 sq ft

Activity 99—Practice Test
1. 4,257
2. 39,702
3. 77 R4
4. 6 hundredths
5. 0.117
6. 1
7. $\frac{4}{5}$
8. $1\frac{13}{24}$

Activity 100—Practice Test

1. $5\frac{3}{8}$
2. $1\frac{1}{2}$
3. $\frac{1}{3}$
4. 40
5. 95
6. obtuse, isosceles
7. parallel
8. 36 m²